14 - 130 - 1498

MARKET STRUCTURE RESEARCH

MARKET STRUCTURE RESEARCH

Theory and Practice in Agricultural Economics

EDITED BY
PAUL L. FARRIS
PROFESSOR OF AGRICULTURAL ECONOMICS
PURDUE UNIVERSITY

IOWA STATE UNIVERSITY PRESS
Ames, IOWA, U.S.A.

PREFACE

E CONOMIC QUESTIONS being raised by many people frequently relate to the industrial organization and performance of the economy. The questions are formulated in various ways, depending upon backgrounds and interests of persons involved. In agriculture there is a common concern as to consequences of developments originating within the marketing sector. Changes in the organization and operation of processing and distributing firms extend beyond the industries in which these firms function and affect both farmers and consumers. Questions encompass such topics as integration, bargaining power, farm income, technological progress, industry efficiency and directions of future change in market structure.

In recognition of these questions a North Central Regional Committee, NCR-20 (Economics of Marketing) was formed early in 1959 to develop conceptualizations and approaches for research on emerging marketing problems. A Subcommittee of NCR-20 prepared "A Report on Market Structure Research in Agricultural Economics," which was published in the Journal of Farm Economics in August 1961. The report presents the nature and analytical framework of market structure research and includes abstracts and references to important writings and active market structure research projects in agricultural economics.

In order to build upon current market structure ideas and to suggest useful ways of applying market structure ideas in research, NCR-20, with support from the Farm Foundation, sponsored a Market Structure Research Workshop on June 18-22, 1962, at Purdue University. The program included formal papers and discussions by leading scholars in the field of industrial organization and performance in agricultural industries. Workshop participants comprised mainly agricultural marketing research workers in the North Central Region and the USDA.

Formal papers and discussions dealt with evaluations and accomplishments of market structure research; interrelations between various influences and market structure, firm organization and industry efficiency; operational criteria for public programs affecting firm entry and exit; and operational criteria for evaluating market performance. The workgroups devoted themselves to selected topics and issues in market structure research.

This book includes the formal papers, discussions, workgroup reports and summary statements presented at the workshop. It is intended as a reference source on market structure ideas, conceptualizations and research approaches. The volume should be particularly useful to educators and research workers who are interested in the industrial organization and performance of our enterprise system, both in agriculture and the general economy.

Members of the Workshop Planning Committee were as follows: George Brinegar, University of Illinois; Robert L. Clodius, University of Wisconsin; Paul E. Nelson, Jr., ERS, USDA; and Paul L. Farris, Purdue University, Chairman.

Lafayette, Indiana   PAUL L. FARRIS

CONTENTS

PART I

Framework

PART II

Impact on Market Structures, Firm Organization and Industry Efficiency

PART III

Operational Criteria

PART IV

Workshop Conclusions

PART V

Summary

PART ONE

FRAMEWORK

Chapter 1

R. G. BRESSLER, JR.
University of California

Research on the structure of agricultural markets

I N THIS DISCUSSION I shall define some of the relevant terms to meet my purposes even though they may depart somewhat from common acceptance. Market organization I shall consider a general term embracing all aspects of the field of research under consideration. Market structure I take to refer in a descriptive way to the physical dimensions involved: the appropriate definitions of industries and markets, the numbers of firms and/or plants in the market, the distribution of plants-firms by size and various measures of concentration, descriptions of products and product differentiation, and of conditions of entry — all of these descriptions, to be sure, geared in some way to our concepts of elements important in affecting market competition. Market conduct refers to the behavior of firms under differing market structures, and especially to the types of decisions that managers can make under these several structures. Finally, market performance I define as the real impact of structure and conduct, as measured in terms of such variables as prices, costs, and volume of output.

SOME HISTORICAL PERSPECTIVES

Research on the organization of agricultural markets with emphasis on the nature of competition had its effective start in the 1930's. Reviews of the scope and method bulletins on Research in Marketing Farm Products, published in 1932, and Research in Prices on Farm Products, published in 1933, support this conclusion. These reports indicate that some 28 percent of the agricultural marketing studies published prior to 1930 were classified under a subfield called "Market Structures" and that 19 percent of the projects active in 1931 and 1932 fell under this classification, but these studies had to do with channels of distribution, the geographic extent of market and supply areas and the historical changes in these physical market characteristics.

1

This is not to say that none of the research projects presented in these two bulletins gives attention to relations between structure, as so defined, and prices. But such attention is rare, and there is virtually no concern with structure and its effects on competition as we view this field today. There is one important exception to this generalization: the discussion of "Monopoly Influences" by John Cassels under Project 28 in the volume on Research in Prices.[1] This is indeed a classic, and I am willing to call it the effective start of our modern work in the organization and structure of agricultural markets. Remember that this article was published in the same year as the theoretical treatments of monopolistic competition by Chamberlin and imperfect competition by Robinson, and predated by three years Burns' empirical study of the decline of competition.

Let me quote a few sections from this article:

... People generally have clung to the belief that the competitive system was being maintained largely intact, until, quite suddenly, within the past few years it has become impossible to escape from a realization of the powerful influence of the monopoly elements in our economic arrangements or to disregard the peculiar and perplexing problems created by their unexpected presence in a "purely competitive" system. Evidence of this change will be found not only in the present-day inclination of governmental authorities toward policies of regulation rather than suppression but also in the tendency for new college courses to be given and new books to be written dealing with the subject of monopoly practices, monopoly prices and monopoly control. ...

The conditions in which monopoly elements are present are many and varied. Where an individual seller or an organized group of sellers is dealing with an unorganized group of buyers, a seller's monopoly is said to exist. Where the buying is done by concerted action and the selling is competitive, a buyer's monopoly exists. If there is unified bargaining power on both sides we have bi-lateral monopoly. If the competitors on either side, although not actually united, are so few in number that they can become conscious of their common interests the conditions are those of duopoly (two competitors) or oligopoly (a few competitors). Where a monopolist, owing to the nature of the product or the condition of the market, is obliged to sell (or buy) all units at the same price he has a simple monopoly but if he has it within his power to charge different rates for units sold to (or bought from) different people or destined for different uses (or coming from different sources) he has a discriminating monopoly. A monopoly which was absolutely unaffected by the competition of substitute commodities (or alternative outlets) would be a pure or perfect monopoly. ... On the other hand, as Chamberlin has shown, monopoly elements are likely to be present even in markets which are commonly regarded as purely competitive. Wherever there are differences, however slight, in the products sold by different competitors or in the services rendered by them the general market will be

---

[1] John M. Cassels, "Monopoly Influences," Research in Prices of Farm Products, Social Science Research Council, June 1933, pp. 154-62.

broken up by the existence of personal preferences into a number of smaller individual markets and we have what he calls <u>monopolistic competition</u>. Between these conditions, in which the competitive elements predominate, and those at the other extreme in which the monopoly elements are most powerful, are all sorts of intermediate cases differing from one another by degrees in which the elements are combined in varying proportions.

Thus we see that Cassels had the main elements of the taxonomy of market organization that is the basis for present work in this field. Moreover, he well recognized the aspects which we have defined as structure, conduct and performance, and the difficulties confronting the researcher in these areas.

In any study of this sort, three steps are naturally involved, concerned respectively with:

1. The existence of monopolistic conditions.
2. The exercise of the monopoly powers thus created.
3. The effect of this monopolistic action on the prices under consideration.

...The first step in any investigation of monopoly influences affecting price will naturally be to study the actual institutions and arrangements found in the market or markets concerned and to determine the nature of the monopoly powers (if any) which are present. This is admittedly a difficult undertaking not only because of the various ways in which the elements may be compounded but also because the type of information needed is not easily obtained.... The investigator will wish to know the extent to which supposedly competing concerns are really subject to some common central authority through the interlocking of directorates, the existence of a holding company, or the ownership of stock by the same individuals. He will wish to know the extent to which the competitors are held together by their common ownership of subsidiaries such as banks, railway lines, storage warehouses, stockyards, terminal facilities, by-product plants. He will wish to know the nature of their agreements with respect to prices, proportions of business, and united action against the intrusion of outsiders into their established markets. He will wish to know the proportion of business done by the dominant individual or group and the extent to which the other smaller concerns, from fear or policy, follow their lead with regard to prices, terms of sale, advertising expenditures, etc.

The next step will be to determine the extent to which the monopoly powers that exist have actually been used to obtain monopoly profits.... care must be exercised to see that the monopoly advantages themselves have not been capitalized and included among the assets of the business on which the rate of return is calculated.... a similar analysis may be made of margins taken, or prices charged.... None of these particular devices taken alone may be sufficient to prove or disprove conclusively that monopoly power is being exercised but when all angles of the situation have been studied and all the evidence pieced together fairly definite results may be obtained.

The final step in the analysis is to determine the extent to which the prices in some particular market have been affected by the exercise of

these monopoly powers. No very precise quantitative results can be expected, but an approximate answer of considerable significance may, nevertheless, be secured — at least in some of the simpler cases.... it must be
recognized that in dealing with such complicated relationships the probability of error will always be extremely high. Not only must the investigator himself bear this in mind continually but in presenting the results
for publication he must also be particularly careful to create no false impression about the reliability or the accuracy of the results obtained.
Where the margin taken by the middleman agency is small, it may entirely
fall within the margin of error of the analysis, and hence render futile any
attempts at analysis.

THE CURRENT STATUS OF
MARKET STRUCTURE RESEARCH

To suggest the present importance of market structure study,
I need only refer to the programs of all recent meetings of the
American Farm Economic Association, or to the pages of the
Journal of Farm Economics. A convenient statistical summary
is provided by a 1961 U.S. Department of Agriculture survey of
marketing economics work (excluding physical and engineering
aspects classified under "Market Quality" and "Transportation
and Marketing Facilities"). This indicates a total of 473 professional man-years of research work in marketing economics, with
about 40 percent carried on by the U.S. Department of Agriculture and 60 percent by the State Agricultural Experiment Stations.
Of this total, some 140 man-years were classified as work on
"Market Structure and Practices," with an additional 26 man-
years on "Farmers' Bargaining Power." In short, more than one-
third of all agricultural marketing economic research now comes
within the field under consideration. Clearly, market structure
research has been and remains one of the most popular fields for
the agricultural economist interested in marketing.

The vast bulk of this work falls under the heading of "Market
Structure" — descriptions of industries and markets, number of
firms, size distributions, concentration ratios and so on. Such
descriptions, coupled with the familiar tableau of market-firm-
product characteristics, permit us to classify market situations —
ranging from competition to monopoly much along lines suggested
. by Cassels. Moreover, these classifications, together with a considerable body of theory, enable us to draw inferences — more
properly, to set up hypotheses — about possible firm conduct and
behavior and market performance. Our success in testing such
hypotheses has been something less than spectacular, for reasons .
again suggested by Cassels.

It is relatively easy to obtain descriptive data on numbers and sizes of firms, and quite difficult if not impossible to obtain pertinent information about managerial decisions, firm policies, behavior and market performance. And so we have too often been content with description — collecting and compiling, classifying and cross-classifying, and devising novel ways of re-expressing the same old facts. Nor is this field completely lacking in the advantages conferred by electronic computation. I find some practitioners now speaking with enthusiasm of powerful and sophisticated new tools, of transition coefficients and Markov chains — by which, I judge from the examples presented, it is possible to take incomplete and inappropriate data and project even less meaningful distributions of firms in the "stationary state."

A Californian would certainly be expected to refer to marketing orders and agreements, where government powers have been deliberately used to modify competitive forces and to create some degree of monopoly power. We can tell you something about the historical origins and provisions of such programs and how program devices have been used. We are equipped with appropriate theoretical models having to do with price discrimination and the controlled distribution of a crop among independent or interrelated markets. But we know little about the effects of marketing orders and agreements on prices and grower returns, either in the short or long run.

Market Organization and Behavior

There are, to be sure, some important exceptions to the generalization that market organization research is largely descriptive. As noted by Cassels, profit ratios may be valuable indicators of conduct and behavior; so we have had a number of studies of profit ratios and of price-cost ratios, with attempts to relate these to particular categories of market structure. My impression is that such efforts have frequently been inconclusive, partially for reasons pointed out by Cassels and partially because of the difficulties in establishing suitable bench marks against which to check observed ratios.

Revealing studies of behavior have been based on information uncovered through the subpoena powers of the government, for these powers do permit intimate exploration otherwise impossible. Studies by the Federal Trade Commission, or based on information derived from FTC hearings, are the classics in this area, although similar materials are sometimes available from other state or federal sources. Even here the results are primarily in

6 R. G. BRESSLER, Jr.

terms of actions and decisions by firms, and still leave much to
be desired in terms of impact on real market or industry performance. The classic study of cartels by Corwin Edwards is a good
example; firm practices documented there read almost like fiction
at times, but how much these practices have distorted the industries from competitive results is not clear.[2]

Market Performance

In the area of market performance, my personal preferences
lead me to believe that the most revealing work has been based on
economic or econometric models. And here it is perhaps appropriate to pay respects to the programmers and computers. I observe with gratification (and with a little amusement) that some of
my colleagues who for years have protested against competitive
economic models in marketing research now eagerly embrace the
transportation model in linear programming, and others who looked
with complete distrust on research labeled "synthetic" now seem
pleased with the new look called "simulation." Let me point out
that virtually all work in the field of market organization is based
on comparison and contrast with competitive situations — the familiar tableau by which we classify market structures, the inferences we draw about the effects of structure on decisions and behavior. Any measure of performance must be relative: how is
industry performance (in terms of prices, costs, outputs, etc.)
modified by a particular structure really means how does performance differ from some other structure; and this other structure is most frequently one closely related to competition.

Our knowledge of performance has been advanced by this approach far more than by the summarization of data on numbers
and concentration ratios. Permit a few examples: in assessing
the performance effects of fluid milk price control, the simple
models used by Cassels and later by Louis Hermann; the more
complicated graphic programming models used by Bredo and
Rojko; and some of the linear programming work by such men as
French and Snodgrass. Others include: in the manufactured dairy
products industries, the perfect market models in space, form and
time developed by Hassler; in California citrus marketing agreements, the work by Hoos by which it is possible to estimate prices
and allocations with no control and with "perfect" control, and to
contrast these results with actual developments; or the dynamic

___

[2] Corwin D. Edwards, Economic and Political Aspects of International Cartels,
Senate Committee Monograph No. 1, Committee on Military Affairs, Washington, 1944.

model of the lemon industry developed by French that permits projections of future cycles with and without prorates designed to influence the fresh market price (this is especially interesting as an effort to discover the longer run effects); and, in tobacco, the work of Maier, Hedrick and Gibson on the sale value of allotments. Obviously, these are only examples, but they do suggest that appraisals of performance are possible, even though I believe that Cassels' warnings about margins of error and "over-writing" in presenting research results are still very much to the point.

CONCLUSIONS

I do not believe that research in market organization is sterile, but I do insist that too much of it has been taxonomic and too little has been directed to the essential questions of the influence of structure on conduct and performance. It is obvious to even the casual observer that most of our industries deviate in dozens of ways from the competitive assumptions; but are these deviations superficial or significant? In 1947 I heard Hayek express the opinion that in 90 or 95 percent of the American economy non-competitive factors were insignificant in terms of real effects and distortion, while in only 5 or 10 percent were such forces important enough to justify governmental intervention. The distressing thing is that, after some 30 years of research in this field, such issues are still the area of opinion and debate rather than having been put into sharp focus by research results.

Agricultural economists have long taken a certain amount of pleasure in criticizing the lack of operational significance in the detailed soil classifications devised by the soil scientists. But we too have our full share of gravel counters and classifiers. In the 1930's, Professor John Hopkins pointed to the lack of correlation between type-of-farming classifications and type-of-farming problems, concluding that if we could expect no more useful results than those at hand we were wasting our research resources in the type-of-farming field. Today I believe that more than a quarter century of research in market organization still leaves this type of problem unresolved. We must do far better in the areas of conduct and performance in our marketing organization research, or we should devote far, far fewer resources to this field. We are in real danger of having developed a meaningless yet professionally respectable field.

PART TWO

Impact on Market Structures,
Firm Organization
and Industry Efficiency

Chapter 2

R. L. KOHLS

Purdue University

*Considerations of internal
firm organization and behavior
factors and their relation
to research on market structures*

I T IS MY DESIRE to add to and not quarrel with the excellent discussion concerning market structure analysis by Clodius and Mueller.[1] In this discussion the authors appropriately point out that many factors may condition the response a firm makes within a particular market structure, and this response will in turn affect the market structure itself. As one of these important possible factors, they propose that "the type of conduct resulting from a particular structure may vary significantly depending upon the internal organization of the firm." This chapter considers some of these internal organization aspects of the firm with the hope that if our research encompasses study of these variables, we can gain a still greater understanding of the dynamics of marketing organizations.

It is the question of "what will happen" in the context of profits, of firm development, of inter-firm channel organization and of organizational innovation that is one of the most important questions asked of market analysts. The central issue of the dynamics of marketing is the response (and the resultant effects of this response) of the units involved in the perceived situation. The pertinent decision-making units in this response are the agencies and institutions operating within the marketing channel. The phrase that "farmers demand" or "consumers demand" a particular change is often used, but is not too fruitful a concept from an analytical viewpoint. It is probably more correct to view the farm (and its product output) and the consumer (and her related household firm attributes) as the permissive perimeters of the marketing system. Changes which occur in the dimensions of these perimeters (and the changes may be either due to factors

*Journal Paper No. 1935 of the Indiana Agricultural Experiment Station, Purdue University, Lafayette, Indiana.
[1] R. L. Clodius and W. F. Mueller, "Market Structure Analysis as an Orientation for Research in Agricultural Economics," Journal of Farm Economics, August 1961, p. 513.

8

exogeneous to the total market system involved or caused by the actions of endogeneous firms in the system) represent latent potentialities of successful operation of the marketing firms. But the questions still remain as to whether the firms in the system will move to take advantage of these potentialities, and if they do, how will they act to take advantage of the situations?

In analyzing marketing firm behavior, many of us with agriculturally oriented background have a major hurdle. The farm firm is a relatively simple firm organization. It is not difficult to pinpoint the decision maker and to detail the organization around him that will carry out the decision. When we move to marketing, however, we move immediately into the area of more complex business organizations. Probably one of the most important single trends overlooked in agricultural marketing is that these firms are, as a group, large and getting larger in the absolute sense. Our challenge then is to accept the fact of large, complex, managerial units as the subject of much of our inquiry.

COORDINATION A MAJOR TASK

The firm (or arrangement of firms) must be viewed as an organization. This organization is a group of individuals which must be coordinated into doing something. It is this coordination issue that is a major task. Theorists in this area basically acknowledge that as soon as the activity becomes large, there are two basic problems: (1) Getting the technical purpose of the organization accomplished and (2) dealing with the problems which arise from the interaction of people who must work together.[2] Both are major problems in and of themselves and each area can affect the performance of the other. Alderson has proposed that we think of a marketing firm (or a group of firms such as those in a marketing channel) as a behavioral system in which there are four subsystems of behavior: (1) the input/output system relating to the specific productive purpose of the system; (2) a power system relating to the actions necessary for survival and status maintenance; (3) a communication system through which information and directions must flow; and (4) an adaptation system which must seek adjustment to internal and external changes.[3]

It is useful to conceive of the managerial function itself as a system of inputs and outputs. On the input side there is the effort

[2]William Gombert, "An Inquiry Into the American System of Industrial Management," Journal of the Academy of Management, August 1961, p. 126.
[3]Wroe Alderson, Marketing Behavior and Executive Action, Richard D. Irwin, Homewood, Ill., 1957.

of evolving a conception of the problem to be solved and assembling
and evaluating the data necessary for establishing possible alternative decision possibilities. After the decision is made, certain
output efforts must be made to get the proper orders passed to
the operational centers and to make sure they are carried out with
a minimum of distortion from the original intent. It is not automatic that firms faced with the same set of situation facts will
make similar decisions — there are the potentialities of alternative courses of action and strategies. Also, even if firms make
similar decisions, the observable action which results need not
be the same — there is a considerable degree of discretion left to
the action group even after the decision as to what to do has been
made.

Hypotheses Proposed

Business organizational and behavioral theory has its roots in
many disciplines, and, at least from my observation, currently
cannot be considered an organized body of thought. Economists,
sociologists, psychologists, historians and even biologists are
currently hypothesizing and observing the important issues of how
decision makers decide, how managers manage, and how organizations organize and change. The literature is full of possibly useful theoretical insights but is relatively empty of empirically
tested conclusions. I would propose four major areas of internal
organizational behavior which if further and explicitly explored,
might yield fruitful results in our research efforts. These are:
(1) Goals of firm behavior; (2) quality of entrepreneurship; (3) information assembly and evaluation; and (4) the control mechanisms
of the firm. I shall state these as hypotheses and discuss what a
review of some of the current literature seems to imply about
each.

Hypothesis: The goals that individual firms hold differ in their
dimensions and details and these differences will influence both
the problem conception and decision making of management.

One of the issues which has a long history of controversy (usually between economists and those oriented more "toward business") is that of validity of the profit maximization goal. Sociologists and others have long criticized as too narrow and constrained
what they have assumed is the economist's assumption of man as
a profit maximizer. Increasingly, however, the debate has been
narrowed as economists have added additional dimensions to the
idea of profit maximization, such as the short and long run,

consideration of risk and uncertainty, etc. Brewster in his recent writings has attempted to narrow this controversy still further by proposing that all that economic theory really presupposes
in its economic man is the maximization of satisfactions; that
man will "rationally" attempt to accomplish his purposes with a
minimum expenditure of time, energy, personal capacities and
other resources. The idea of monetary profit is an unnecessary
restriction which has been added in evolving literature.[4]

Shubik follows this theme by cautioning that a firm consists
not of <u>homo economics in vitro</u> but of many men embedded in a
market in society. Therefore, we must consider the possibilities
of these individuals having goals which may be somewhat different from the goals of the firm as an operating unit. Also, the
firm as a unit may have economic goals of operation as well as
goals guiding its interrelationship with other firms and the rest
of its politico-socio-environment.[5] Leibenstein emphasizes that
the goal of a firm is not predetermined by outside overriding factors, but rather is determined internally by the organization itself.[6]

Baumol recently has proposed that large corporations do not
have profit maximization as their goal, but rather the goal is one
of total revenue expansion limited by a minimum level of acceptable profits. His principal thesis is that this attitude is largely a
result of the separation of management and ownership in a large
corporation. Minimum profits are necessary to keep stockholders
happy; a growing corporation is easier to manage personnel-
wise.[7] Penrose echoes this position when she proposes that firms
desire to make money largely for the purposes of reinvestment
and growth and only secondarily to pay stockholders.[8]

Cyert and March in their studies of organizations and their
goals caution against expecting to find too much. They maintain
that since business organization is essentially a coalition of individuals, at best there will be agreement upon a highly ambiguous
set of goals. They state that studies indicate that business goals
often take the form of aspiration levels rather than an imperative

[4] J. M. Brewster, "Belief, Values and Economic Development," <u>Journal of Farm
Economics</u>, November 1961, p. 781.
[5] Martin Shubik, "Objective Functions and Models of Corporate Optimization,"
<u>Quarterly Journal of Economics</u>, August 1961, p. 375.
[6] Harvey Leibenstein, <u>Economic Theory and Organizational Analysis</u>, Harper and
Brothers, New York, 1960.
[7] W. J. Baumol, <u>Business Behavior, Value and Growth</u>, Macmillan Co., New York,
1959.
[8] Edith T. Penrose, <u>The Theory of the Growth of the Firm</u>, John Wiley & Sons,
Inc., New York, 1959.

to maximize or minimize something.[9] A further extreme from
this is taken by other writers who caution that it is possible that
organizations do not have specific goals, but simply react and behave in response to a given situation guided only by some rough
criteria for determining satisfactory behavior.[10] Closely related
to these propositions is that the goals of large firms, presumably
because of the more individuals and resultant viewpoints involved,
tend to be more multidimensional than small ones.[11] Goals, also,
may not be static over time, but may change with the evolving
growth, diversity experience and size of the firm.[12]

The most usual listing of goals which may exist in some degree and may vary somewhat, or be in addition to the simplified
profit maximization idea would include the following:

(1) Expand or grow in size
(2) Maintain or enhance status or power
(3) Control the important related parts of a business —
    a drive for closure of the system to secure greater
    independence from the market or other firms
(4) Survive — very few managements choose to quit
(5) Simplify or improve the management and handling of
    personnel in a firm — or at least not upset a satis-
    factory operating situation.

Regardless of the position in this argument we take because
of our background and disciplinary biases, we certainly must admit that the goals of a business as conceived by the managers of
that business may be of major importance in affecting both how
the firm will conceive its problems and how it will react to a
given situation. There is enough uncertainty over what these
goals might be and what factors might cause a difference in goals
to justify research attention to the issue.

Hypothesis: The quality of entrepreneurship differs among firms
and these differences influence the behavior of firms.

There has been an attempt by several to differentiate between
managerial competence and entrepreneural competence. Often
this effort at separation seems to be synonymous with the common
conception of "levels of management," such as line and staff
structure, or with the kind of decisions involved, such as strategic

[9] Mason Haire, editor, Modern Organizational Theory, John Wiley & Sons, Inc.,
New York, 1959.
[10] Leibenstein, op. cit.
[11] Shubik, loc. cit.
[12] A. H. Cole, Business Enterprise in its Social Setting, Harvard University
Press, Cambridge, Mass., 1959.

or routine. But these classifications do not adequately describe
the effort to separate the problem of entrepreneurship.

Managerial competence seems to be those skills and functions
which get the job done in a complex organization setting — or, as
Penrose says, of holding the firm together and operating its resources.[13] Much of the organizational theory which deals with
personnel relations, motivations of employees, etc., apparently
falls largely in the category of "managerial skill."

Entrepreneural competence, however, is the bundle of attributes that the major decision makers must have which sets the tone
and direction of the total firm operations. Someone must search
for new opportunities and perceive the economic need to initiate
action. There must be creativity in the sense of seeing new opportunities and problems and insuring that the proper and necessary activities are set in motion so that these opportunities can
be evaluated. The entrepreneur also furnishes the connection
with history in the firm, for each decision furnishes the foundation and background of the succeeding ones.[14]

We know (or believe) intuitively that certain firms are very
conservative while others are very venturesome in their attitudes
toward possible new situations. We also recognize that some are
the initiators while others are followers. (And incidentally all of
these various firms may fit into the category of being "excellently
managed.")

What causes these differences in entrepreneural attitude to
develop, persist or change? Economic historians have maintained
that simply passing time has much to do with such differences.
Past history and experience tend to predispose the current entrepreneur toward a certain attitude. Experience is an input into the
development of entrepreneurship, and therefore, the entrepreneural
resource tends to grow and change.[15] Cole has suggested that
there is a chronology of entrepreneural orientation. In its infant
or beginning years the risk of business mortality tends to focus
its attention inward on the operation of the firm itself. After the
firm passes this test and begins to grow, the entrepreneural interest broadens out first to local community concerns, then to its
role as part of the industry and finally to its potential relation to
the national interest.[16] In these latter two stages a high degree of
"like thinking" develops among entrepreneurs of similar firms
and a high degree of imitation and faddism is likely as firms respond to changing conditions.

---

[13] Penrose, op. cit.
[14] Cole, op. cit.
[15] W. W. Rostow, The Stages of Economic Growth, Cambridge University Press,
New York, 1961.
[16] Cole, op. cit.

Others propose that entrepreneural differences arise simply because of a diversity of temperaments of people and of the cultural, social and educational background from which the entrepreneur is drawn.[17] Size and the technology used by the firm also may have an influence on the nature and quality of entrepreneurship. This would be particularly true if it leads to the dominance of a select management group in the firm's operation, such as in finance, marketing and sales, production engineering, etc.

The writings in this area are stimulating but are still exploratory and confusing. However, two conclusions seem to come forth which can strengthen our research in firm behavior: (1) The quality and dimension of top entrepreneurship do vary and this variation can influence both problem conception and decision making and (2) some possible variables in determining this difference may be age and history of the firm, background of the entrepreneur, the nature of operation and organization of the firm itself and the absolute size of the firm.

Hypothesis: The availability of pertinent information necessary or available for problem conception and decision making will vary from firm to firm and this will influence the behavior and reaction of firms in a given situation.

The one issue upon which most students of the theory of firm behavior and decision making agree is the central and primary role of information seeking and evaluating activity. Information must be gathered so that decision makers can make decisions. The information may be either plentiful and accurate or inadequate and faulty. The process of its collection and evaluation may be highly formal or very informal. However, incomplete information is the usual state of business affairs. The question is how vigorous and how successful will the firm be in its actions to reduce the area of ignorance or misinformation.

Some authors propose that the problem of getting adequate information at a reasonable cost is one of the major motivating reasons why firms decide to internalize (or seek closure of) a series of operations rather than take direction from the market place in the form of market prices. It is proposed that one of the limitations to a firm's growth is the decline in efficiency which may occur from the division which size makes necessary between the activities surrounding the informational activities and the actual decision-making activities. In a small firm entrepreneural, information-seeking and managerial functions may be closely coordinated — often in one person. In a large firm this is not possible. Therefore, following this line of reasoning one of the

---

[17] Gombert, loc. cit.; Penrose, op. cit.

possible explanations of variation of rates of return among firms is that firms vary in their effectiveness of collecting, simulating and using knowledge. [18]

Penrose, on the other hand, assigns a central role to the information problem as a causal agent of growth. She proposes that a firm in its growth gradually acquires a bundle of managerial services (which would include skills in making information useable and effective). Larger firms can devote more resources to the selecting of the problems which are important and to obtaining and evaluating the pertinent information. In this fashion the uncertainty of results from future actions can be reduced. The general impact of the argument is that growing firms tend to have built into them both an automatic increase in knowledge and an incentive to search for new knowledge.[19] Size and growth also make feasible the utilization of the technological improvement in information gathering and analysis made possible by the machine and computer development.[20]

Many writers have suggested that one of the factors which will influence firm behavior is the availability of resources which can be used for planning purposes. When such resources can be saved from the pressures of day-to-day operations, information will be more timely and will be more usefully evaluated. This accumulation of excess talent which can be used for planning and thinking may be one of the prerequisites for expansion. Interestingly enough, this leads to the proposition that expansion and growth of a firm may come about without any overt management decision to expand and grow. It simply yields to the pressure which develops from a growing pool of unused planning and informational resources.[21]

We have noted above how the information problem may be one of the forces pressuring for vertical integration. In this same vein, there may also be motivation for growth by acquisition of operating units. When a firm purchases such a unit, it buys not only the operating and physical facilities and skills, but also the developed skills which may be available in the firm for acquiring and evaluating the information necessary for wise decisions.

This brief excursion into the causes of variation in information processes indicates some contradiction in the writings in this area. This seems to be the case. However, there is wide

[18] H. B. Malmgren, "Information Expectation and the Theory of the Farm," Quarterly Journal of Economics, August 1961, p. 399; Shubik, loc. cit.

[19] Penrose, op. cit.

[20] C. E. French, "The Management Resource and Agricultural Marketing," Journal of Farm Economics, December 1961, p. 1265.

[21] Haire, op. cit.

agreement on three propositions: (1) information gathering and evaluating activities are necessary to the operation of large firms; (2) such activity has a cost; and (3) various firms evolve different ways of handling this problem which seem to have some interaction with the decisions and actions which the firm takes and with the future level of entrepreneurship.

Hypothesis: The degree and effectiveness of putting decisions into action vary among firms and this will influence the behavior and reaction of a firm in responding to a given situation.

One of the most evident problems in a large business (and widely discussed problems in organizational theory) is how to effectively control and direct it. The top entrepreneural group may know precisely the goals to be reached and be well endowed with creativity, insight and willingness to take risks. The system to collect and evaluate the needed information may be adequate and working well. However, getting the decision accurately transferred to the appropriate place and securing the desired action presents another set of problems.

A business organization is a group of individuals which must be coordinated into accomplishing the task of the organization. These individuals must be recognized as having two separate interests — those associated with the accomplishment of their assigned tasks and those associated with their existence as a person that wants status, recognition, security, etc. In almost any organization there must be some degree of discretion left to the individual at each level of the management structure. Such conditions help explain why there may be considerable inconsistency between the goals and intentions vocalized by upper management echelons and observed behavior and results of the firm.[22]

The case study of A & P by Adelman presents an excellent case in point. Hartford, the president, had a goal of a good return on investment and believed that the route to this was low margin, low prices, high volume and turnover. However, in spite of this high level purpose, from 1919 to 1929 expense rates rose and gross margins increased. Various top management efforts to reverse this development failed. Only after a crisis in 1936-38 did the lower echelons begin to accept and apply the basic idea of low margins and prices which had been the continued policy of higher management.[23] This seems to be an excellent example of "behavioral drift" — a slow and undirected shift in actual operations which

---

[22] Leibenstein, op. cit.
[23] M. A. Adelman, A & P: A Study in Price-Cost Behavior and Public Policy, Harvard University Press, Cambridge, Mass., 1959.

develops in spite of orders and directives, largely because a firm is operated by human beings and human action tends to change.

Much of the literature of organizational theory deals with various hypotheses of how best to organize for effective control. Practically all agree that this is the area in which size of the organization has a real impact. Businesses develop into a bureaucracy in which there are increased formal and fixed ways of doing things. Dimock proposes that the management of any particular firm has in it two elements: the enterprise or entrepreneural activity whose job is to innovate, change and progress; a bureaucracy whose function is to stabilize, control and systematize.[24] As a firm grows older and bigger, its operative system may tend to become routinized and formalized. Under such conditions a decision made at top level to move in a different direction from the established pattern may be distorted or dampened down by the time it is transmitted to the action perimeter of the firm.

Management either through habit or intent arrives at an estimate of the degree of sensitivity of direction that exists in its lower echelons. It is quite conceivable that decisions to take action which might be beneficial are consciously not made because of the recognition of the high cost or difficulty of communicating the order and getting it properly carried out. It is common observation that some firms are more adaptable and innovation-minded than others. Part of the explanation may lie in the effectiveness of the internal system of communication and control.

The information and communication lines of a company are looked upon as a two-way street: Information from the action fronts (market problems, operational problems, etc.) should be passed upward so that they can become pertinent decision-making information and the orders and directives from these decisions must be passed down to the action points. Authority functions through communications. If we accept the idea that a large firm is really a coalition of individuals each with a role to play, and each with motivations and goals which may be partly in agreement but also partly in some conflict with others in authority, then the potentiality of the channel of communication not working effectively is substantial. One of the obvious weaknesses here is that lower echelons may pass on to higher echelons only that information which past experience has shown will be acceptable or beneficial to the transmitter.

Dubin has proposed that these communication links between units of an organization are at the same time both the essence of organization itself and its weakness. He hypothesizes that if strength and flexibility of an organization were a desired goal,

---

[24] M. E. Dimock, Administrative Vitality, Harper and Brothers, New York, 1959.

then the system should organize with the fewest communicative links possible.[25]

From even a passing review of the extensive literature in this area, it would appear that explicit study of the nature of the internal organization of a company and its system of communication and control might lead to additional understanding of firm behavior. Form of organization, age and size may be important variables in affecting the ability of top entrepreneural management to direct the activities of the company. They may also be important variables affecting the accumulation of important information which is available for decision making.

IMPLICATIONS TO RESEARCH ON FOOD MARKETING STRUCTURE AND BEHAVIOR

The purpose of this discussion has been to stimulate consideration of the possibility that intra-firm conditions may be important determinants in inter-firm behavior and to suggest a possible way of grouping these conditions which might facilitate research. Some might argue that all these conditions are merely the result of the external market structure which a firm faces. That some interrelationship between these internal behavior and external pressures may exist need not be denied. It is quite true, however, that the more traditional, market structural characteristics at best often set rather wide boundaries for the behavior and actions of firms. They often give up little indication of patterns of firm growth and organizational innovation. Research which specifically explores the intra-firm areas discussed above, therefore, may considerably improve our ability to predict in a more precise fashion future firm behavior and market structure.

The body of literature covering these intra-firm issues is growing and coming from diverse sources. There is an obvious lack of empirical testing of many of the propositions. Many, I am sure, would have preferred a chapter such as this to explore and recommend specific research projects and work to be undertaken in this area. This activity I would propose is the next step down the road. We must first answer the challenge of utilizing our ability to collect and synthesize these many bits and pieces of insight and knowledge into some workable models specifically oriented to our marketing needs. We then can collect meaningful data and evolve methods of analysis (and both these areas present new problems and challenges) which will permit empirical testing in the industries with which we have established rapport and contacts.

---

[25] Haire, op. cit.

Chapter 3

ALLEN B. PAUL
U.S. Department of Agriculture

Capital, finance and market structure —two approaches*

T HIS CHAPTER TREATS capital first as an external and then as an internal market factor. Each approach can handle some of the same problems — yet each has a different orientation and asks a different set of questions. Each approach has something useful to say about the organization of production and the functioning of markets.

CAPITAL AS AN EXTERNAL ASPECT OF COMMODITY MARKETS

The "market structure approach" is classical in orientation: A market centers on some product or service and comprises buying and selling forces that determine output, price, returns and the like. Capital and financial markets are external and to be taken into account only when they seem to limit the adjustment of commodity firms. This follows from the concept that abstracts the firm from its net worth.

In classical theory, this gap in realism is taken care of by two other constructions, namely, that the world is certain and, in a perfect market, any amount of real capital can be commanded by the firm by borrowing at the going rate of interest. Since the world is really uncertain, and borrowing is indeed limited, two further constructions are used — a risk-premium on the interest rate to take care of defaults and capital rationing to take care of differences in borrowers' and lenders' ideas of how much money should be loaned at the going rate of interest, including a risk-premium. These ideas are not always explicit, but they are always implied.

*The Views expressed here do not necessarily reflect those of the U. S. Department of Agriculture. Benefit from the critical review of William T. Wesson is acknowledged.

The market structure approach embraces these constructions. The task here is to see what questions the market structure approach can answer. I will treat three topics concerning the bearing of capital and finance on market structure. They are barriers to entry, causes of mergers and financial cost disadvantages. Topics concerning imperfections in markets for items of physical capital, although of great importance, cannot be managed here.

Barriers to Entry

Capital for an efficient operation has tended to become larger and this creates problems. Unfortunately, we are short of systematic studies for the food industries. One would have to assemble various data, published and unpublished, and interpret them in a common framework. The gaps would have to be filled with supplementary inquiries. Short of this, one can only speculate on available evidence concerning capital requirements and financial capacity. I will venture a few observations.

1. In appraising whether capital requirements are a barrier to entry, one has to make several value judgments. Wherever it is judged important to have a certain set of firms in the market — such as family enterprise, small corporations, farmer cooperatives, local firms or some other set — then capital requirements become a social problem if the needed capital for "efficient" production tends to rule them out. But where the value judgments emphasize "efficiency," a problem arises where existing firms become secure from new competition because of capital requirements.

2. The question of who can mobilize capital is not governed strictly by size of firm. Any growing firm, whether small or large, has too little command over capital to take up all its investment opportunities. Mueller and Garoian point out that most large food chains could enter food manufacturing because their profitability enables them to mobilize the necessary funds.[1] This seems plausible since most lines of food manufacture have modest capital requirements compared to the net worth of large chains. Yet, a point to be stressed is that in the past these chains appear to have become "loaned-up" in the post-war race to modernize and expand into the suburbs. I suspect that most firms in the top 20 could not have commanded the capital to enter into many new lines of food manufacture in this period without

[1] W. F. Mueller and L. Garoian, Changes in the Market Structure of Grocery Retailing, University of Wisconsin Press, Madison, 1961, pp. 84-85.

sacrificing their long-run competitive positions as food retailers. They would have missed out on important locations. Thus capital might have been a ruling barrier to enter into manufacturing.

3. The economic system can mobilize large doses of capital where such investment appears attractive. Firms on the periphery of an industry, with lesser opportunities at hand, might be expected to enter. However, the deterrent may not be so much the large capital requirements as the condition which it portends — the fear of lowering the prevailing profit rate by adding the capacity. A contest to gain market acceptance at a competitor's expense can be one of the least rewarding uses of capital, unless the firm has a better product or a lower potential cost. In these cases, one anticipates entry by firms capable of mustering the capital.

Where market growth is expected to absorb the new capacity well, new entry is not ordinarily blocked by the scale of investment. The appearance of temporary overcapacity in various industries is suggestive.

4. Yet, absolute capital requirements do pose problems for society. The grounds for concern are not always clear. I do not think that an absolute reduction in number of potential entrants is itself the problem — except where there are value judgments concerning who should be able to enter an industry. Relatively few potential entrants may be all that are needed to achieve acceptable performance. It is rather fruitless to talk about absolute capital requirements as barriers to entry, other than in a mechanistic sense, out of context of specific industry situations. For what it is worth, Professor Bain speculated that capital requirements of over 10 million may present, in some cases, an added barrier to entry. But he hastened to add we know virtually nothing about its importance.[2]

One can speculate that the assurance of effective competition requires entry of "fresh blood" into an industry. The problem is to determine how this is to be achieved. Do we need a large supply of young growing firms? Where such firms are merged into larger firms, does this serve the purpose? The market, left to its own devices, eschews new firms where capital requirements are large — except where profit prospects are large, as in shopping centers. The latter is a Henry George type of exception. How adequate are the frontiers for small enterprises? Should we get concerned about various foreclosures on opportunity? Perhaps what is needed is a systematic study of individual business

---

[2] J. S. Bain, Industrial Organization, John Wiley & Sons, Inc., New York, 1959, p. 252.

histories to shed light on such matters, for they will continue to
exist.

Mergers and Acquisitions

While a firm may acquire another firm to gain a strategic
market position, or to balance enterprises, the question here is
somewhat different: Do firms acquire other firms because of
capital problems?

1. A true merger — combining two companies through exchange of stock or issuance of new shares — clearly may overcome the limitations of having too small a capital under one management. Some added flexibility in use of resources becomes
possible with attendant production efficiencies. Also, portfolio
management in the face of market uncertainties may be handled
with better effect.

Even if the acquiring firm pays cash — where the presumption
is that the capital at the command of the acquiring firm is not enlarged but is merely rearranged — the exchange might improve its
perspective earning power and therewith its ability to borrow
more effectively than before the acquisition.

2. An acquired firm may have sold out because of difficulties
of mobilizing additional capital for long-range expansion purposes. A small growing firm that manufactures a specialty food
line may not be able to broaden out or modernize without a larger
dose of capital than it can arrange in the market. Its most attractive alternative may be to become a subsidiary of a large, financially strong firm. Are such conditions, wherein retained earnings of the large firm are the most effective source of capital to
the small growing unit, the best conditions for the economy at
large? What are the feasible alternatives? Perhaps the experiences of the recently formed Small Business Investment Companies (SBIC) will teach us something about the possibilities and
pitfalls of devising workable arrangements.

3. An unprofitable small firm may sell out — as a business,
rather than piecemeal — because a deficit is a salable asset under
modern tax law. Profitable small firms may sell out because
their discounted income prospects may be converted to a current
capital gain. Thus, tax law is a key to understanding market
structure.

Professor Butters noted that the tax system exerts powerful
pressures on owners to sell out or merge. They may have to meet
liabilities arising out of estate taxes, or to value the business for
tax purposes, or to minimize their personal income tax and the tax
on unreasonable accumulations of corporate surpluses. Thus,

when a business is sold or merged, the profits can be withdrawn as capital gains and not as dividends. These consequences might argue for some overhauling of the tax system to remove a needless cause for mergers.[3]

4. I do not know how compelling each of the foregoing considerations has been in changing industry structure. They seem to be researchable topics.

The Cost and Availability of Loans

An important fact about the food marketing system is that roughly one-half of the business is conducted by firms too small to enter national or regional markets with their own security issues. Firms with less than from one to three million dollars in total assets (or perhaps less than 1 million in net worth) usually cannot enter such markets at reasonable cost.[4] They would have to pay too much to underwriters and others. Similarly retailers seeking to enter long-term leases on store properties may find no takers.[5]

Such firms incur higher costs because small security issues bear relatively high overhead charges and partly because they pay premiums to cover larger-than-average credit risks. The cost of raising funds by public means tends to rise precipitously with firms that grade downward from the level of the one million dollar asset size. (Figure 3.1.)

Firms with less than one million in assets pay from one to two percent higher interest rates when they borrow from bankers than large corporations. And when risks are judged too high, small firms might have to turn elsewhere or go without.

We can classify, tentatively, food marketing firms based on certain economies of scale in finance. If we take one million dollars of net worth to be a rough dividing line between firms large enough to price their securities in the national and regional markets, and firms that must be content to work out local financial arrangements (e.g., with banks, equipment dealers, suppliers, customers, or certain specialized financial intermediaries), the following distribution of sales in 1958 is evident (Table 3.1).

The column on the left includes sales of corporations having

[3] K. Butters, "Taxation, Incentives, and Financial Capacity," American Economic Review, May 1954.

[4] G. W. Mitchell, "Review of Survey Findings," Financing Small Business, Vol. I, Part 2, 1958.

[5] Lease Guarantees — 1961, Hearings, Select Committee on Small Business, United States Senate, 87th Congress, 1st Session, December 1961.

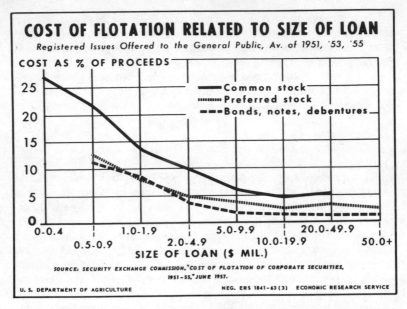

Figure 3.1. Cost of flotation: Registered issues offered to the general public, 1951, 1953, and 1955.

under one million dollars net worth and the sales of all partnerships and sole proprietorships. While some noncorporate business may have over one million in net worth, the error introduced by this seems negligible. If it is true that local financial markets tend to be somewhat imperfect and relatively costly to deal in, then a sizable share of the food industry is so exposed. The majority of distribution and a substantial share of processing are involved.

Table 3.1. Percentage of Sales by Business Firms According to Their Estimated Net Worth, 1958*

Sector	Under one million dollars net worth	One million dollars and over, net worth
	Percent	Percent
Food manufacturing and beverages	28	72
Food wholesaling	68	32
Food retailing	60	40
Total	48	52

*Based on Internal Revenue Service data.

The issues and problems to which these facts give rise may be briefly summarized under the following points:

1. Small firms usually pay higher interest rates and this is a distinct competitive disadvantage. Yet, if such rates merely reflect the higher costs and hazards of doing business with small borrowers, the competitive disadvantage is no different in principle than other cost disadvantages of small firms. It is a general problem facing society. A special problem might arise wherever interest charges to small firms exceed the costs of lending. Presumably, an examination of the loss experience of lenders, by size of borrowers and sources of borrowings, would show where and to what extent this were a genuine issue.

2. The rationing of loans to small business by means other than interest charges may be a problem — especially for deserving concerns. The rules of thumb for lending by banks may not give due weight to the earning power of a capable management. In many food businesses personal acumen is one of the most important income-producing assets. But it is not easy for the highly institutionalized lenders to measure.

For this and other reasons, the rise in importance of trade credit enters. The extension of credit by one business to another has become a greater part of the competitive calculus. What lenders would be in better positions to evaluate the income-producing and debt-paying power of a business than its suppliers? One would doubt that any large number of deserving businesses would be overlooked for long. Yet, there may be important deficiencies, which makes this area worthy of study.

3. The availability of long-term funds is a particularly difficult problem for small firms. While venture capital from individual and pooled accounts is available to small business, the food industries have not been particularly attractive — except shopping center properties. Instead, such investors look to high-gain industries with large prospective pay-outs — such as electronics. Evidently, the loss experience has been sufficient, even after a careful screening of applicants, to make the over-all return only moderately attractive.[6]

In long-term borrowing the small firm usually must post collateral. The mortgaging of real estate is the usual way of doing this. Also, considerable equipment is financed through leasing.[7]

---

[6] "Availability and Costs of External Equity Capital for Small Business Ventures," Financing Small Business, Vol. II, Part 2.

[7] The rapidly growing lease-financing companies provide business firms with items ranging from shopping carts to derricks. While the banks, insurance companies and foundations do not lend freely against the security of equipment of small business firms, they lend considerably to lease-finance companies against a batch of lease contracts posted as collateral. Such intermediation of finance brings into the over-all loan operation not only a specialized servicing of leases but also an actuarial structuring of the credit hazards, which makes such lending feasible.

How adequately the long-term borrowing needs to small food
manufacturers are met should be judged in light of the fact that
their net borrowing already tends to be quite large. This may explain why long-term loans to small business are not ordinarily
provided on an unsecured basis.

4. The case for small retailers is somewhat different. Com-
plaints have long been registered that successful independent grocers frequently cannot secure prime space in shopping centers unless they have one million or more in net worth. This seems to point
to a serious deficiency of the financial system because, unlike processing, command over sites and financing is bound together.

The modern food retailing business is unusual in the sense
that a modern supermarket can be put into operation with a relatively modest capital fund — around $500,000. Large supermar-
kets do not ordinarily bring down unit costs. Presumably there
might be about as much income produced by 50 independently
owned supermarkets as by 50 supermarkets owned by one firm —
assuming each group were serviced by comparable warehousing
and buying arrangements.[8] In the chain, store managers are hired
and the stockholders get the return on equity, whereas in the independent group, the store owners earn a management as well as
an equity return. Conceptually, the debt-paying power of each
group might be alike. But the 50 independents would have a serious financial disadvantage, which makes their very existence
problematical. Outside investors may have legitimate doubts
about the wisdom of a particular store site or reservations about
the continuity of a particular management. In a 50-store chain,
these doubts would fade because a few errors in location or weaknesses in store management would not ordinarily impair the
firm's ability to make good on all of its leases.

The search is for an actuarial method of implementing a public program that would be self-financing and have a minimum of
unwarranted side effects.[9] It is a moot point whether there are
still substantial economies of scale in the private chain-store
organization that cannot be matched by cooperative and voluntary
groups. If so, the need to solve the problem of lease guarantees
for the independent owner becomes a critical problem in the future organization of this industry.

5. Finally, the financing of farmer cooperatives poses special problems. Historically, growers sought to provide some essential services through pooling their capital — either services
that were not offered privately or if offered, not acceptable.

---

[8] However, the chain may be able to benefit from financial maneuvers (e.g., realty
deals) by having the net worth of the system under a unified control.

[9] Lease Guarantees — 1961, op. cit.

The institutionalization of lending to co-ops — through the Bank for Cooperatives — has been a notable achievement in mobilizing loan funds efficiently. Evidently, the reserve lending power of the Bank is substantial. But a recurrent problem is to attract more venture capital into the cooperative endeavor where the local business situation warrants such investment. This is a knotty problem and needs to be integrated with grower-financing of the operations of the cooperative through various participation plans in which each patron shares in the proceeds, at a deferred date.

6. These few observations point to deficiencies in the arrangements for mobilizing capital — some of which are serious and seem amenable to improvement. Many useful contributions to their understanding and solution can be made by economists concerned with market structures. The research task is to gauge the forces causing changes in the behavior of financial markets and to determine where conscious improvements might be sought.

One can be aware of the shortcomings of the system and yet be impressed with the ingenious ways in which financial accommodations have been worked out over the past four centuries in the face of extreme complexity and difficulty. This perspective is too easily lost. Professor Commons tells us that "it required the entire Seventeenth Century for lawyers to complete the invention of the negotiability of debts" and that it took "all of the centuries following to invent ways of making this kind of promise negotiable."[10]

For example, small firms operating in the food industries are not always at a financial disadvantage, thanks to special institutional arrangements that have arisen to meet their need. Small firms may borrow relatively large amounts at relatively small cost where the system assures repayment. Thus, loans up to 90 percent of the cost of commodities frequently are obtained through brokers or banks, when warehouse receipts can be put up as collateral and a positive mechanism exists for closely gauging the margin of safety and liquidating the collateral should commodity prices change adversely. Organized commodity futures trading is a prime example of just such a mechanism that puts the smaller firm on a par with large firms, financially speaking.[11]

---

[10] J. C. Commons, Institutional Economics, The Macmillan Co., New York, 1934, p. 292.

[11] According to Paul and Wesson, it can be observed that wherever there is active futures trading, the market (properly identified) includes many small independent firms that use it directly or indirectly. But where a market consists of mostly a few large firms, there is no room for organized futures trading and none exists. Furthermore, wherever futures trading can be instituted, it is in itself a force that tends to improve the competitive position of the small firm — enabling it to mobilize more capital than otherwise — and hence increase its economic viability. (A. B. Paul and W. T. Wesson, "The Future of Futures Trading," Futures Trading Seminar, Vol. I, Minier Publishers, Inc., Madison, 1960.)

CAPITAL AS AN INTERNAL ASPECT
OF COMMODITY MARKETS

The concept of capital as an external aspect of commodity markets has a major limitation. Professor Boulding, one of the most able expositors of classical theory, put the matter bluntly as follows:

> ...My main cause for dissatisfaction with the existing theory of the firm lies in its deficiency in capital theory. The usual marginal analysis treats the firm as if it had nothing but an income account; it has no balance sheet, no capital problems, and no dynamics; ...[12]

If the concept of the firm were not abstracted from its capital structure, then capital would not be external to commodity markets. The firm is indeed more than a converter of inputs into outputs. It is also in command of an equity fund that may be committed in different ways. The behavior of firms is governed by both production and ownership considerations, and not by either alone.

This is a different way of examining commodity markets than that to which we have become accustomed. It provides a more meaningful approach to understanding market structure and behavior — including the means by which market structures change — than do classical conceptions.

Balance-Sheet

The central economic idea is the balance-sheet. It is a set of items of value classified as assets, liabilities and net worth. Everyone with some economic sovereignty has such accounts, although not necessarily formalized on paper. Such balance-sheets are not closely matched by accounting statements — although the usual aim in accounting practice is to get as close as practicable to the economic idea.

Entries in the economist's concept of the balance-sheet reflect a scheme for distributing ownership rights, couched in terms of the prevailing institutions. Assets consist of claims to various considerations of value, reflecting existing uncertainties: They include not only claims on titles to physical items, but claims to future use of, or yield of items. Deferred claims include those fixed in commodity units such as leases and contracts for deferred

---

[12] K. E. Boulding, A Reconstruction of Economics, John Wiley & Sons, Inc., New York, 1950, p. viii.

delivery; claims fixed in money units such as notes, bonds, trade accounts and so on, and claims to residual values of business, such as partnership and corporate shares.

Presumably each economic unit tries to achieve some preferred asset combination. Differences in asset preferences among and between households, firms, associations, syndicates and governmental units cause exchange to occur. Such exchange influences the organization of production and this is what we wish to examine.

Because ownership rather than physical goods is transferred in exchange, the idea, born of classical conceptions, that commodity markets and financial markets are separate is not tenable. A market includes all opportunities to buy or sell to which an economic unit has access. Exchange involves more than commodities and money, it involves claims defined in terms of money, commodities or residual enterprise shares. The present concept is a market in assets and not a market in commodities. It is general in that it is not restricted to purchases or sales of any item or class of items.

Market Boundaries

One may ask: How is it possible to establish the boundaries of a market when so broadly defined? Is it operational? The answer is yes, provided we do not make rigid boundaries. The approach does not specify the precise limits in advance; rather these are left open to be fixed later as more knowledge of a particular commodity sector is acquired. Thus, to investigate the economics of a particular commodity sector, we need to identify the economic units whose purchases and sales in the asset market "explain" the commodity economics. The units in this set depend on the particular research question, but the set would never be limited, as under the classical conception, only to suppliers and demanders of the commodity.

For example, to explain the commodity economics of potatoes we would want (as a minimum) information from potato dealers, fertilizer firms and machinery firms concerning their buying and selling and their borrowing and lending as related to the potato business. Similar information would be needed from potato growers and some other firms engaged in related physical operations. Also, the operations of banks, other lending agencies and commodity speculators would need to be known. In short, an explanation of the commodity economics of potatoes, as visualized by the balance-sheet approach to markets, includes in addition to

activities of potato growers and distributors, the activities of producers of related physical services, financial intermediaries, investors, input suppliers, banks and other lenders.[13] In contrast,
the classical approach would have research into financial questions and physical operations in the potato market treated as separate and not as essentially interrelated issues; e.g., how are
potato dealers financed? how do potatoes move through channels?

Unfortunately, little work has been done to adapt the balance-
sheet approach to analysis of commodity economics.[14] This could
be due to the traditional practice of separating "real" and "monetary" analysis. Professor Hart states that this separation is the
economists' logical reaction to muddled thinking by laymen, saying that "money has been pictured as merely a 'veil' which
shrouds the true nature of the economic system." But he also
thinks that this reaction "went dangerously far, and for some
years now, economists have been busy correcting its excesses."[15]
The corrections, however, serve mostly to elucidate the role of
money — as revealed by writings of Hicks, Hart, Marschak,
Gurley, Shaw, Tobin, among others.[16] Yet cogent ideas on commodity economics are to be found among these works.

Boulding used the balance-sheet approach in his Reconstruction of Economics, but his main interest was to elucidate the aggregative behavior of prices, wages, employment, profits and so
on, by using asset preference theory. He made a suggestive start,
however, for further study of commodity economics with his for-
mulations on the theory of asset choice.[17] So did Markowitz in his
analysis of optimum portfolios.[18]

Two major difficulties must be met if the balance-sheet approach to analysis of commodity markets is to be operational.
First, it requires some revision of customary ideas on capital,
ownership, enterprise, finance, output, prices and so on. This is
necessary to explain how specialization of production is actually

[13] W. T. Wesson, Economic Importance of Futures Trading in Potatoes, Marketing
Research Report No. 241, United States Department of Agriculture, 1957.

[14] The work, conducted by The Brookings Institution, by Rowe, Paul and Wesson on
the explanation of organized futures trading in commodities, developed a particular
approach. (Paul and Wesson, op. cit.) In a somewhat different vein, Professor
Lachman used such an approach in his study of capital. (L. M. Lachman, Capital
and Its Structure, London School of Economics, 1956.)

[15] A. G. Hart, Money, Debt, and Economic Activity, Prentice-Hall, Inc., New York,
1948, p. 2.

[16] J. R. Hicks, "Suggestion for Simplifying the Theory of Money," Economica,
February 1935; Hart, op. cit.; J. Makower and J. Marschak, "Assets, Prices, and
Monetary Theory," Economica, August 1938; J. G. Gurley and E. S. Shaw, Money in
a Theory of Finance, The Brookings Institution, 1960; J. Tobin, "Money, Capital, and
Other Stores of Value," American Economic Review, May 1961.

[17] Boulding, op. cit.

[18] H. Markowitz, "Portfolio Section," Journal of Finance, March 1952.

achieved under the cumulative enlargement of the market. Second, we need empirical information on (a) a wide range of market transactions and (b) trade practices. I shall suggest some lines of thought concerning the first of these difficulties.

Purpose of the Financial System

A financial system fosters a more productive use of resources. As Professor Boulding pointed out:

> ... The principal function of the financial system is to separate the ownership of real capital from its control, that is, to enable people to administer real capital without owning it, and to own it without administering it. ... If there were no financial system ... every person would have to administer the real assets which he owned, no matter how incapable he might be at such a task. The financial system has grown up because the *personal ownership* of real assets is a result of a long process of historic accident, through individual saving and inheritance, the structure of which need bear no relationship to the structure of administrative abilities or economic needs.[19]

It is in the above sense that the welter of financial claims of a modern exchange economy can be best understood. In a growing economy, more people exchange their surplus above consumption for claims to future income, rather than use the surplus in production themselves. The institutions of ownership change in the course of over-all economic growth. From a social viewpoint, these institutions may be judged by how well they foster the productive use of resources — i.e., the potentials for specialization of production, economies of scale and the application of technology. The problem is to discover ways of appraising financial institutions in the light of these criteria.

Assumption of Enterprise Responsibility Economic activity is primarily generated by those who hold equity positions and not by those who hold debt. The persons who stand to gain or lose from the commitment of resources to a course of production are enterprisers. They are responsible for the bill of goods that society produces. Thus, the financial system not only separates the ownership of real capital from its administration — as Professor Boulding noted — but it also allocates enterprise responsibility. That is, the owners may choose between accepting a fixed money return, geared solely to time-preference, and a residual return geared also to an enterprise calculus.

The classical conception visualizes enterprise responsibility

---

[19]Boulding, op. cit., p. 276.

as risk-taking with compensation for potential losses. The effective return to all owners of capital comes down to the rate of interest adjusted for risk-premium. Thus, the problem of allocating
enterprise responsibility is cast into too limiting a framework.

The idea of enterprise advanced above is crucial to understanding the organization of production in the real world. It comprehends all the ways in which someone can influence the course
of production through purchase and sale of assets, including those
which delegate decision making to hired managers.

The Idea of Enterprise Organization   The usual idea of enterprise organization concerns the form of the business unit — the
terms under which the "going concern" (in Professor Commons'
language) is established by proprietors. Included are various
family businesses (still important in farming, retailing and res-
taurant trades), partnerships, cooperative associations, private
corporations and government corporations. All are ultimately
sanctioned by their owners; all preside over the use of purchasing power — the net worth commanded by the organization. The
nature of the transaction between the owner and user of this purchasing power is a significant event because it sets the character
of the going concern as we observe it. Hence it is pertinent to the
idea of enterprise organization.

At least two other major means of organizing enterprise in
agricultural commodity sectors — cutting across firms, households and government — are often overlooked. One is the forward
contract and the other is the joint account. Enterprise commitments made under these usually call for production of specific
goods or services.

Forward contracts occur in a wide variety of forms. A common characteristic is that prices are fixed up in advance of delivery. A cattle feeder often reserves range cattle months before
roundup; bakers generally order flour for delivery several months
ahead; exporters buy futures against advance purchase orders for
grain from importers; processors, distributors, trade intermediaries and people generally anticipate demand for a commodity and
take forward positions in the light of their needs; the government
makes extensive commitments through price supports to take
commodities at future dates. In each case, the significant event
is the commitment of purchasing power of one party to take delivery of and pay for a bill of goods and the commitment by another party to see that such goods are in fact forthcoming.

Examples of joint accounts occur between farm operator and
landlord, feed dealer and livestock producer, vegetable grower
and shipper, shipper and receiver, beet sugar processor and
grower; between groups of farmers to process and market their

own produce; between groups of retailers to buy, warehouse and transport their supplies, and so on. In each case, the significant event is the agreement to put some part of the net worth of each party into a specified undertaking and to share, in some agreed way, in the proceeds.

Enterprise Conditions Needed for Specialization of Production
Partnership and corporate arrangements mobilize capital and place it under a unified command. Generally these arrangements favor the specialization of production, enlargement of plant scale and application of technology, but this is not necessarily the case.

Less widely appreciated are other conditions that enable firms — small and large — to rationalize production. They permit the firm to maintain enterprise balance while specializing production. To learn what constitutes enterprise balance — the ownership positions that permit the firm to remain viable in an uncertain world — one should study the bearing of the asset and liability composition of differently situated firms from the standpoint of yield and yield variance.

It may be sufficient here to note that the maintenance of enterprise balance, under changing conditions, rests on a financial system that provides adequate means to split up an enterprise undertaking (without, of course, splitting up the physical operation itself) and allows the different parts to be transferred readily among market participants according to their individual needs and preferences.

In this context, the forward delivery contract and the joint account acquire their essential economic meaning. While the partnership and the corporation are equal or proportionate-share arrangements, in which all owners are in the same boat, the forward contract — and often the joint account — are unequal-share arrangements under which the participants have different responsibilities and outcomes.

The benefits to the buyer of the forward contract come, in context of his other commitments, from assuming responsibility for transferring the commodity through time (i.e., producing a future good out of a present good); whereas the benefits to the seller come from producing and marketing the services used to transfer commodities in time, place and form. Since forward contracts can be quite selective, it becomes possible to fix up in advance terms which call forth quite specialized production of the services needed to transfer commodities in time, place and form.

Joint accounts also are flexible arrangements for dividing up enterprise responsibility. But unlike forward contracts the outcomes for the participants are frequently interdependent, though unequal; that is, one party makes more profit if the other party makes more profit. The exact bearing of joint-account arrangements on the degree of specialization depends upon their specific terms. Presumably the potential for increased specialization is large.

The Idea of a Price for Productive Services

The link between enterprise division and specialization of production, as discussed above, is largely through price. But the idea of price needs elaboration. The exchange of certain assets establishes certain prices and enterprise positions. When some enterprise positions become paired, the marketing of a bundle of productive services is implied and a price for the bundle is established.

We commonly say that a price for a commodity implies a price for the bundle of services used to produce the commodity. By the same token, the difference between the price for deferred delivery and the price for spot delivery of a commodity represents the value of a set of services required to turn the spot commodity into the deferred commodity. This indirect pricing of services is the same in principle as the direct pricing of services — e.g., sale for an explicit fee of warehousing, transport, milling, livestock fattening, and so on. But the identification of the bundle of services is more difficult when it is marketed indirectly through commodity transactions.

The simplest transfer is through time. Holbrook Working's early studies of wheat gave empirical content to the idea of a market-determined "price of storage" — including the idea of negative prices for storage services not wanted.[20] The same idea of price applies to transfers in place and form. Thus, the spread between spot and forward delivery may be a price for some combination of services to transfer a commodity in time, form and place.

Since different combinations of services might be used to get a certain result — e.g., different places of storage might be selected in combination with different shipping or processing services to produce an item conforming to a given time, place and form specification — the spot-forward price spread is usually a price for some different combinations of productive services. Hence, if several price spreads for several variants of the commodity were available, one might infer the price for individual services in the bundles by cross-section study.

---

[20] H. Working, "Theory of Inverse Carrying Charges in Futures Markets," Journal of Farm Economics, February 1948.

Prices for services provided under joint-account arrangements can be understood in similar terms when the returns to a participant are fixed in advance. Thus, when farmers agree to raise cattle for fixed sums per head, these amounts constitute prices for bundles of service. If there were some variations in the composition of service bundles that were provided by different farmers, the prices for individual services in the bundles might be inferred by cross-section study. However, if the gross returns to a party have not been specified in advance, but are determined by the outcome of the venture, such returns are a residual rather than a price.

Illustrations of Enterprise Organization

The early growth of the vegetable canning industry in Wisconsin illustrates enterprise-sharing that was "internalized" almost wholly within the trade channel. Machinery and construction interests promoted the needed capital. Local share-equity and bank loans were arranged. Sometimes the machinery interests took notes in partial payment. The canning firm then mobilized working capital by (a) sharing with farmers the outcome of the canning venture — i.e., cost and profit sharing, toll canning or deferred payment on grower contracts without means of assuring payment and (b) by selling most of the anticipated pack to wholesale grocers, sometimes even before the seed was planted, under firm price and quantity agreements. These commodity contracts formed a basis for borrowing — to meet operating expenses, particularly when the pack was made and could be posted as security.

Thus, from rather lean beginnings, a specialized canning industry in Wisconsin was developed over several decades by sharing the prospective gains with commodity businesses that were able to shoulder the output, price and credit hazards. Losses were frequently sustained and many canning ventures failed. These losses would have hurt, but usually would not have destroyed either the grower (a dairy farmer) or the wholesale grocer (a diversified-line operation).

Today we may observe similar enterprise organizations of other sectors — e.g., poultry, eggs, beef — wherein the enterprise-sharing is essentially internalized within the commodity trades. In the picture are growers, input suppliers, processors and distributors as well as various specialized loan intermediaries.

At some stage of development, enterprise-sharing arrangements cease to be internalized within the physical channel. A fund of outside equity is brought into play through forward

contracts and joint accounts. As a result, specialization of production may be further intensified. While the exact nature of the
outside equity fund and the way it becomes committed may change
over time, its bearing on the organization of production does not
change, although its effectiveness might.

The Maine potato-growing industry, which has become more
intensively specialized over the decades, has passed through three
stages in mobilizing "outside" equity through enterprise-sharing
arrangements. In the early stage, from about 1870 to 1940, Miller
showed that merchants, fertilizer dealers and starch factories
bought potato "futures" from growers for delivery at harvest.[21]
Probably not all contracts were held for the accounts of these
trade interests; undoubtedly others took advantage of opportunities
to buy potatoes cheaply for speculation.

From 1942 to 1949, government price-support loans were offered potato growers, constituting forward purchase commitments
with the public equity. The effect on production was stated by Gray,
Sorenson, and Cochrane as follows: "With the government guar-
anteeing a market, the natural response of specialist producers
was to expand and intensify potato production."[22]

The third stage emerged with cessation of CCC commitments.
Wesson's study showed the financial reasons why organized futures trading in Maine potatoes, which had only a tenuous life in
the 1940's, developed into large proportions in the 1950's.[23] There
is no difference, in principle, between specialization of production
resulting from government price guarantees and from private
price guarantees — although there might be major differences in
actual outcomes.

A simplified chart of the different ways in which such "outside" equity might be committed to production, under different
enterprise-sharing arrangements, is shown in Figure 3.2. The
flow of money loans, as a result of making such enterprise commitments, is also suggested.

THE FIRM AS A LOAN INTERMEDIARY

While our discussion to this point has submerged the role of
debt commitments to the role of enterprise commitments in

---

[21] C. J. Miller, "The Development of the Potato Marketing System in Aroostook
County, Maine," Harvard Studies on Marketing Farm Products (Unpublished).
[22] R. W. Gray, V. L. Sorenson, W. W. Cochrane, The Impact of Government Programs on the Potato Industry of the United States, North Central Regional Publication No. 42, University of Minnesota, 1954, p. 6.
[23] Wesson, op. cit.

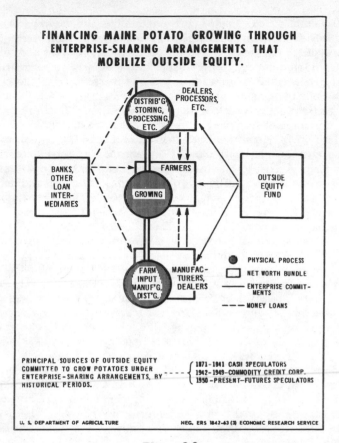

Figure 3.2.

generating economic activity and influencing the organization of
production, it would be wrong to assume that debt commitments
have a minor bearing on production. The making of debt commitments is not automatic but depends on fitting the institutional
means to business needs. Since most arrangements have emerged
by trial and error over a fairly long period, while conditions war-
ranting such developments themselves change, some deficiencies
must be expected. The flow of capital into production may be im-
paired, productive organization may not be the most efficient possible, and the competitive character of the market may be seriously affected.

The first problem is to get an adequate conception of the loan
machinery for a commodity sector. According to the usual conception, one would focus attention on specialized loan intermediaries

— e.g., commercial banks, insurance companies, savings and loan firms, pension funds, installment credit houses, factories, government lending agencies and so on. As a whole, specialized loan intermediaries have grown relative to the economy, suggesting a causal connection.[24] But what usually is missing from the picture is the role of nonspecialized loan intermediaries — i.e., the average firm engaged in commodity production. Little is known about this and yet it seems to be of great importance.

Almost every commodity business is a loan intermediary as well as a producer. Only part of the purchasing power commanded by the firm is used to buy inputs for current production. Part is used to provide open accounts to customers, hold demand deposits for continuity of operations, short-term securities for prospective outlays and long-term securities for unforeseen contingencies and future expansion. Every business lends as well as borrows and is, to such extent, a financial middleman between savers and users of the economic surplus.

In the food sector, financial assets in 1962 were about 40 percent of total book assets in processing; about 50 percent in wholesaling, and 35 percent in retailing and eating places. Receivables were the main item, except for food retailing and eating places which held more cash. Together, receivables and cash formed about two-thirds of the financial assets of the entire food marketing sector (Figure 3.3).

Commodity businesses in food now play a larger role in the process of financial intermediation than in the immediate pre-World War II era. Is such growth of nonspecialized financial intermediation by food firms an aberration? Or does the over-all growth process necessarily involve commodity businesses in more financial intermediation, as the economy expands?

Differently situated firms show different experiences. For example, big food processors drew down cash and did not expand customer credit, relatively speaking. This suggests either that customer credit is a more important competitive weapon to medium and small processors, or that in the post-war expansion and modernization big firms chose to skimp on expanding financial assets. The latter suggests that such expansion has merely been delayed. In either case, we may gain insight into markets through such reasoning about finance.

The pressure for funds also shows in gross borrowings. Large processors increased their debt relatively more than smaller processors (Figure 3.3). Of course, they could do so because they had less debt. The increased borrowing by big firms came

---

[24] Gurley and Shaw, op. cit.

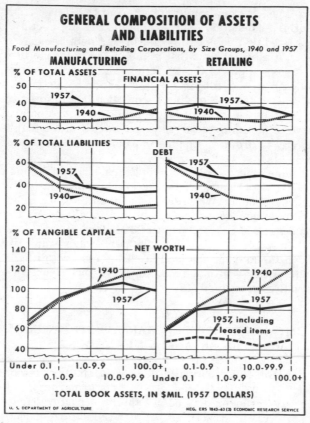

Figure 3.3. General composition of assets and liabilities, food manufacturing, and food retailing corporations, by size of groups, 1940 and 1957.

from virtually every source — accounts payable and short-term notes, bonds and other long-term debts and other liabilities including tax accruals.

The difference between financial assets and debt is net borrowing (or net lending). The net condition may be shown as net debt in relation to physical capital, or, more understandably, as the obverse. If firms required funds only to get resources for production, the simple relation of net worth to physical capital would show the surplus or deficiency of the proprietary account for such purposes. The data in Figure 3.3 are somewhat surprising in this respect. Large firms increased their net borrowing while the smaller firms stood pat. We know that small firms do not have sufficient equity to work with and make use of extensive

borrowed finds, but one might not suspect that large firms would
show similar tendencies. The explanation is not certain. It has
been suggested that business firms prefer debt because of the tax
treatment. It also appears that some of the increase in debt is
accrued taxes — a gift of the system in the form of an interest-
free loan. About one-fifth of the increase in gross borrowings by
large food processors took this form. It might also be true (contrary to common belief) that large processors had no available
alternative in the immediate post-war period other than to borrow
more heavily in order to finance expansion. These are proper
subjects for investigation.

A further thought applies to retailers. The inclusion of estimates for lease obligations gives a much more realistic picture
of the degree of debt: While there apparently was a substantial
increase in net borrowings by most retailers between 1940 and
1957, the degree of indebtedness of different-sized firms appears
to be rather uniform. All are heavy borrowers — just like public
utilities. If the market has evaluated the food retailing business
as a public utility — with assured markets and assured yield — is
this evaluation warranted?

IMPLICATIONS FOR "MARKET STRUCTURE"
AS AN ANALYTICAL IDEA

The foregoing discussion implies a particular idea of market
structure: at any given time, production, ownership, enterprise
and exchange arrangements each exhibits structural features.
Thus, production is structured through the nature of physical
operating units; ownership is structured through complex patterns
of equity and debt claims; enterprise is structured through various enterprise-sharing arrangements; and exchange arrangements
are structured through a body of custom regulation, law and facilitating services. Market structure, then, is the totality of such
separate structures.

This is obviously quite a different idea of market structure
from that advanced by Professor Bain and largely discussed by
other writers in this volume. I think it is more relevant for
studying important changes in agricultural commodity markets
than that advanced by Bain. The latter analysis rests essentially
on neo-classical foundations and is subject to its limitations. The
firm has no balance-sheet and the market is confined to the prod-
uct(s) of the firm. The scope for inquiry then does not go much
beyond number and size of firms, ease of entry and product differentiation, on output, prices and profits. Analysis deals mainly

with departures from "equilibrium" positions, which implies that market organization is stable. No limitations on obtaining capital at a price are recognized other than "imperfections" of the loan market.

The neo-classical approach can of course accommodate changes in market organization. And its use might suggest needed changes — e.g., as when output and prices depart from those dictated by an "efficiency model" as argued by Professor Bressler and his colleagues. Nevertheless, the existence of a continuous process by which change in market organization is generated is not implicit in neo-classical models.

There is warrant for believing that the alternative ideas suggested here provide a basis for a more relevant concept of market structure. Change is the overriding feature of commodity markets as evidenced, in the case of food, by the profound changes during the past several decades in physical and financial methods in the conduct of farming, assembly, transport, storage, manufacture, wholesaling and retailing. All indications are that such changes will continue.

Classical doctrine given by Adam Smith and elaborated by Allyn Young[25] and others provides us with insight into how the process of change is related to growth. In brief, viewed over a long period, the growth process is self-generating and is predicated on the continual reorganization of production by more efficient methods. Market enlargement is usually based on further specialization of production, lowering of costs and release of resources to be used in new ways. As one industry expands, it furnishes an enlarged market for the output of other industries which then find it feasible to further rationalize production. The latter industries tend to grow and furnish enlarged markets to still others. And so the process feeds on itself with the potentials for specialization, economies of scale and applications of technology all becoming heightened. Industry after industry becomes caught up in the need to modernize, write off old equipment, retrain personnel, make different products and so on — or eventually decline.

This is a big concept. If one could harness market enlargement with the ideas about capital and finance that are available, we would take a major stride toward realism in identifying and analyzing marketing problems. The idea of capital is at the very foundation of market structure. The growth of output and the growth of capital are different facets of a larger phenomenon.

---

[25] A. A. Young, "Increasing Returns and Economic Progress," The Economic Journal, December 1928.

Capital, as Professor Knight once said, is "productive capacity
viewed as a quantity."[26] Markets become restructured only as
new decisions are made on how capital is to be used. It is a root-
process of society that decides the nature of marginal changes in
competing forms of production; it is capital and its yield-rate to
which all economic decision making, both private and public, may
be made intelligible.

The movement of capital to more productive uses is not automatic — it depends on enterprise possibilities. These possibilities
change with the growth and specialization in markets and with the
evolution of exchange arrangements. These exchange institutions
affect the way in which economic decisions appear in the economic
system. Thus, ownership, enterprise and exchange arrangements
have their own structural features which, in the final analysis,
determine the type of performance — e.g., enterprise-sharing arrangements that satisfy basic production and ownership problems
arising in each industry, that lead to lower unit cost or improved
products by further specialization, scale economies and technological advance.

Some Directions for Inquiry

The directions for inquiry are implicit in our discussion. We
know so little about the actual enterprise organization of many
commodity sectors that it would be worthwhile to make some
basic descriptive studies, including longer historical accounts.
Similar information is needed on the intermediation of debt. The
aim of such studies would be to determine the bearing of changes
in institutions that separate ownership of real capital from its
use on changes in production.

For example, one might examine particular growth points in
the food economy and see how capital was directed there and the
consequent rearrangements in production. Soybeans, safflower,
irrigated cotton, citrus, frozen fruits and vegetables, processed
potatoes, commercial mixed feeds, food retailing, among others,
are eligible. Questions to be answered are these: Who made the
enterprise commitments? What means were used to subdivide
and transfer the parts? How much money debt was issued? What
obstacles had to be overcome? Was there further specialization
of production or enlargements of scale? What were the returns
to enterprise and to lending? How did these ownership positions

---

[26] F. H. Knight, "Schumpeter's History of Economic Analysis," Southern Economic Journal, January 1955.

fit into the respective balance-sheets of investors? What were their alternatives?

Thus, if we could get a grasp of the interconnections between the institutional world and the "real" economic world, we may get insight into the most relevant possibilities for the future organization of a commodity sector.

A particularly interesting idea arises from the increasing socialization of the responsibility for employment and income. Uncertainty about the aggregate demand for food becomes smaller. Analogously, farm commodity programs may have reduced the uncertainty over prices for food as materials. Do not such events change the organization of production?

A key to the answer is the resulting tendency to narrow the economic difference between debt and equity claims. The less the uncertainty over outcome, the less the distinction means. Hence, two resulting tendencies can be visualized. One is to attract venturesome savings into nonfood areas where opportunities appear brighter. The other is to speed change within food industries themselves — i.e., to develop or exploit economic frontiers, as in specialization, enlargement of scale, new locations, new technology, new products and services, and so on. What, in fact, has been the connection between reduction in basic uncertainties facing food industries and the hastening of change?

One problem is knowing whether basic uncertainties have in fact declined. For example, too much can be attributed to some commodity programs that largely supplant other institutional arrangements. And in some situations, the basic uncertainties may have increased — perhaps onion growing and merchandising being a case in point since the termination of organized futures trading. Also, uncertainties may have been injected by the operations of the very commodity programs themselves — e.g., with respect to grades, locations and availability of stored commodities.

But where basic uncertainties have declined, one should be able to see how production was restructured. There are studies that suggest the general nature of the problems under discussion — e.g., the Gray-Sorenson-Cochrane potato study, the Hathaway bean study, the Zellner raisin study, the Jones lettuce study and the Brookings futures trading study, among others.[27] The general ideas are capable of considerable elaboration and extension.

---

[27] Gray, Sorenson, Cochrane, op. cit.; D. E. Hathaway, The Effects of the Price Support Program in the Dry Bean Industry in Michigan, Michigan Agricultural Experiment Station, 1955; N. Townshend-Zellner, Federal Raisin Market Order: Impact on Industry Returns, Adjustments, Marketing Structures, and Practices (To be published as a United States Department of Agriculture Technical Bulletin, late 1963); W. O. Jones, "A Case Study of Risk Distribution," Journal of Farm Economics, May 1951; Paul and Wesson, op. cit.

Chapter 4

DANIEL C. WILLIAMS

Carroll, Williams, Rulison,
Conan and Ryan
Syracuse, New York

Labor organizations and their relation to market structure and industry efficiency

L ABOR ORGANIZATIONS exert their influence on the economy largely through collective bargaining and political action. The latter is outside the scope of this chapter. The influence through collective bargaining on a particular business is felt in four areas: (1) wages, (2) fringe benefits, such as holidays, pension plans, etc., (3) working conditions and (4) the operation of a system of industrial jurisprudence and representation within the company or group of companies.

Labor unions can be characterized as "strong" organizations, embracing approximately one-third of the nonagricultural labor force and protected by favorable federal and state legislation. This legislation is administered in turn by fairly sympathetic, if not sometimes militant, bodies such as the National Labor Relations Board. The union's basic economic weapon — the strike — is indeed a mighty power, feared in different ways by the large or oligopolistic employer and by the small employer in a highly competitive position. Unions furthermore have imposing assets of national and community acceptance, money, intelligence, membership loyalty and in some cases, a large spirit of militancy.

It comes as a surprise to some that this great power has not been wielded in such a way as to affect substantially the economic institutions of the country to any important extent or to introduce the millennium to union members. The studies of Levinson, Johnson, Denison and others have made it fairly clear that organized labor has not succeeded in the past years of power in increasing substantially its relative share of the national income or in diverting profits into wages.[1] To the minor extent that labor has

---

[1] H. M. Levinson, "Collective Bargaining and Income Distribution," American Economic Review, Papers and Proceedings, XLIV:2, May 1954, pp. 315-16; D. G. Johnson, "The Functional Distribution of Income in the United States, 1850-1952," Review of Economics and Statistics, XXXVI:2, May 1954, pp. 175-82; E. F. Denison, "Distribution of National Income: Pattern of Income Shares Since 1929," Survey of Current Business, 32:6, June 1952, pp. 16-23.

received an increasing share of the national income, it seems
fairly well supported in the literature of the field that collective
bargaining by unions by itself has played only a secondary role.[2]

Why has there been such a small net beneficial effect resulting from all this mighty power? To discuss this question will
undoubtedly throw important light on the subject of this chapter.
Clark Kerr has suggested that unions do not have the incentive
nor the power to get deep enough into the decision-making process of business to redirect the profits to themselves. To do so
they would have to cripple the executive power of the owners to
act freely, or they would have to have the support of a national
system of price controls.[3] Unions hesitate to take either step.
The "golden goose" of our economic system has laid a good many
golden eggs for most groups in this country over the recent years
and the unions don't want to kill it; even if they wanted to, the
rest of the population doesn't seem disposed to let them.

The relative share of the national income going to labor has
probably been kept relatively stable by the ability and freedom of
employers to introduce labor-saving devices and to raise prices.
This drive on the part of business to keep pace with the pressure
on the wage level has undoubtedly been heightened as the wage
pressure has increased. As early as 1935, Hicks suggested that
this would happen.[4]

Furthermore, the power of companies to resist unions is far
from inconsiderable. Striking a company exerts a tremendous
toll on union and employee savings. Pressure on the head of a
family not to strike is strong, especially if some wage increase
has been offered by the company. Many believe that the unquestioned wage-raising power of unions derives mostly from easy
credit policies and the natural inflationary bent of our economy.
The unions, according to some, are merely leaning on the un-
latched door of fiscal-monetary policy.[5]

Others, to be sure, give to the union a more positive and
powerful initial role in forcing up wages and prices. For instance, the business community as well as those who have the
responsibility for fiscal-monetary policy, such as the party in
power, naturally does not want to place the blame for inflation
on itself; and some economists, in fact, do blame unions as the

---

[2] Levinson, op. cit., pp. 315-16; Johnson, op. cit., pp. 175-82; Denison, op. cit.,
pp. 16-23.

[3] Clark Kerr, "Trade Unionism and Distributive Shares," American Economic
Review, Papers and Proceedings, XLIV:2, May 1954, pp. 283-88; 291-92.

[4] J. R. Hicks, The Theory of Wages, Macmillan, London, 1935, pp. 198-99.

[5] C. L. Christenson, "Variations in the Inflationary Force of Bargaining," American Economic Review, Papers and Proceedings, XLIV:2, May 1954, pp. 357-62.

prime mover in the wage-price rise. Probably Slichter,[6] Hicks [7] and Beveridge[8] belong somewhere in this area. A further group, probably a distinct minority, ascribes to unions such a surplusage of monopolistic power as to threaten rampant inflation and the destruction of our free system.[9]

The best that can be said about this basic assessment of union power is that the evidence is not all in; some responsible people feel that there would be a waste of considerable time and money in more arguing or researching about it.

EFFECT OF UNIONS ON MARKET STRUCTURE

The foregoing observations seem to apply when we view labor union strength from the standpoint of its effect on market structure. The effect of the union seems limited. If you assumed that unions had a vast impact on market structure, you would expect that it would reveal itself typically by enforcing a uniform high labor cost on all enterprises in a particular industry. The inefficient producers would thus be forced out at a quickening rate. New companies would be deterred from entering the field. Enterprise would be choked off; a bad national "product mix" might also result, especially from distortions of "normal" relationship among occupational rates.

However, this has not happened generally in our economy; as a matter of fact, the structure of an industry seems to have much more effect on organized labor than does the reverse.

The ability to pay high wages in an industry is probably the real prime determinant in paying such wages, rather than union pressure. At least the wage differences that can be observed between industries seem to be based on the ability to pay; and that in turn seems to be based on the state of the competition in the product market.[10]

---

[6]S. H. Slichter, "Wages and Prices," Proceedings of the Academy of Political Science, Columbia University, XXIII:1, May 1948, pp. 47, 60.

[7]J. R. Hicks, "Economic Foundations of Wage Policy," Economic Journal, LXV: 259, September 1955, p. 391.

[8]William Beveridge, Full Employment in a Free Society, Norton, New York, 1945, pp. 198-99.

[9]C. E. Lindblom, Unions and Capitalism, Yale University Press, New Haven, 1949, pp. v, 22, 35-36, 138-39, 146-49; H. C. Simons, "Some Reflections on Syndicalism," 1944 in Economic Policy in a Free Society, University of Chicago Press, Chicago, 1947.

[10]J. W. Garbarino, "A Theory of Interindustry Wage Structure Variation," Quarterly Journal of Economics, May 1950, pp. 282 ff; L. G. Reynolds, "The State of Wage Theory," Annual Proceedings, 1953, of the Industrial Relations Research Association, p. 240.

Professor Kuhn puts it this way:

Many products in the United States are, of course, sold under intense competition. Whether unionized or not, these industries typically do, in fact, pay wages about as low as their respective labor markets permit. But other products sell under highly administered markets, and many show an inelastic demand to boot. Here certainly the ability to pay high wages prevails. Again, whether unionized or not, this is the kind of industry which typically does, in fact, pay high wages, and its firms must be presumed to be free to give the benefits of rising productivity to their employees if they care to.[11]

Other writers in the field tie wages expressly to the productivity of the industry, without respect to its competitive structure.[12]

Although some industries have a high degree of unionization, such as basic steel, automobiles, aircraft, rubber and meat packing, there are many fields in which there are enough nonunionized companies to dampen the wage-raising power of the unions over an industry. Whether a company bargains by itself or in association with others, it will bargain with one eye on the wage rates paid in the nonunionized segments of the industry. So must the union.

Unions are often unable to completely organize an industry on a national scale. For instance, employers in the South still pay lower rates of wages in all but those industries having a national or interregional product market. Regional differences in labor productivity, living costs and product markets all blunt the drive for uniformity. Both union and management must likewise have due regard to the threat of product substitution.

In the face of all this, and mindful that their members are highly job-conscious, unions often make concessions to the firms faced with high competition. Wage gaps are often closed only gradually. "Historical differentials" are observed. Fringe benefits, such as elaborate pension plans, are deferred or installed only gradually. The individual workers, in turn, do not leave for the higher-paid jobs in the higher-paying plants.

Even in situations where there is association bargaining on a regional basis or state- or city-wide basis, accommodation seems to be the order of the day. The tendency is not to force the weak out of business. The weak make sure their interests are represented in association bargaining. The strong employers may often, of course, have an interest in high wages; by this device

---

[11] Alfred Kuhn, "Market Structures and Wage-Push Inflation," Industrial and Labor Relations Review, January 1959, p. 247.
[12] S. C. Sufrin, Union Wages and Labor's Earnings, Syracuse University Press, 1950.

they can force weaker firms out of business. But the stronger
impulse is to be moderate. Most strong employers usually like
a low common denominator of wages. A majority position is usually established at a level at which most can survive.[13] "Wisdom,"
"moderation" and "understanding" are words you read in descriptions of union and company attitudes in industry-wide or
association-wide bargaining. These are the kinds of attitudes
which help the weak stay in business.[14]

Although one would expect to find uniform rates of pay under
conditions of association-wide bargaining (even though these
rates are moderated), nonuniformity is often introduced to protect those at a competitive disadvantage.[15] Geographical differentials are sometimes allowed so that lower wage rates balance
off excessive freight rates to the central market. This technique
has been observed in bargaining in bituminous coal, men's and
women's clothing factories outside New York, silk and rayon dye-
ing and flint glass.

Some association-wide bargaining has achieved the same result by providing for a wage bargain expressed in terms of uniform rate changes, rather than uniform wage rates. Thus differentials enjoyed by marginal firms are preserved. Other industry-
wide bargains are expressed in terms only of a uniformity of
minimum rates. Here the marginal firm pays the minimum and
the better situated firms can pay premiums above the minimum.
That has been observed in the pottery industry, photo-engraving
and some bargaining in the women's and men's clothing field.

This description of labor's power and its limitations in raising
wages must lead to the inevitable conclusion that organized labor
has little effect upon product market structures. I know of no
research that has indicated they can have much effect. This
chapter, therefore, must necessarily deal with exceptions to that
hypothesis. There do seem to be these exceptions.

Structure Preserved by Unions

I turn first to those situations in which the union positively
seeks to preserve the product market structure when the structure

---

[13] Clark Kerr and Roger Randall, "Collective Bargaining in the Pacific Coast
Pulp and Paper Industry," Industry-Wide Collective Bargaining Series, University
of Pennsylvania Press, Philadelphia, 1948.

[14] Otto Pollak, "Social Implications of Industry-Wide Bargaining," Industry-Wide
Collective Bargaining Series, University of Pennsylvania Press, Philadelphia, 1948,
pp. 53-54.

[15] Thomas Kennedy, "The Significance of Wage Uniformity," Industry-Wide Collective Bargaining Series, University of Pennsylvania Press, Philadelphia, 1948,
pp. 17-32.

is monopolistic or oligopolistic. Machlup describes this in the
following words:

> Unions do not attempt to break the business monopolies of the firms
> with which they deal; they avoid doing anything to reduce the degree of mo-
> nopoly that the firms have in their selling markets. On the contrary, unions
> may seek to increase and consolidate these monopolistic positions. We
> know of many cases where a union has succeeded in "organizing" the em-
> ployers, in limiting competition among them and in protecting them from
> "chiseling" newcomers. This is sometimes done by making sure that no
> potential competition can obtain the necessary supply of labor or materials.
> Successful union-management cooperation in restraining competition among
> business firms has been described in many court cases in which the Govern-
> ment charged violations of the antitrust laws. But the aid which a union may
> give to established business firms in their efforts to limit competition need
> not take such sensational forms. Much less conspicuous methods will often
> be even more effective. For example, the adoption by a national trade
> union of a uniform wage standard for the entire industry can effectively
> eliminate new competition from areas in which the competitive wage level
> is lower because of differences in labor efficiency, natural resources or
> capital endowment. Through such wage standards the unions protect the
> established business firms from newcomer's competition. That trade unions
> frequently give also political aid to the maintenance of monopolistic posi-
> tions of their industries through high protective tariffs is an old story.
>   The effects of such interplays between business monopoly and labor
> monopoly are not compensatory but additive. The output restriction by the
> monopolistic enterprise will usually be more drastic after the monopolistic
> labor union accomplishes its objective. For once, the protection which the
> union secures for the monopoly position of the firm will permit the latter
> to pursue a bolder price policy. In addition, whatever the demand situa-
> tion, the increased labor cost will be an incentive to still sharper output
> restriction and higher prices. True, the workers employed in the firm
> will have become sleeping partners sharing in the monopoly profits of
> their employer; but the restriction of production will be more serious
> than before, at the expense of other laborers and consumers. [16]

In the past we have found collective bargaining agreements
which have bound employers to a certain price level. There has
been price fixing included in collective bargaining contracts with
barbers and beauticians, in wholesale bread and milk distribution,
and in the construction business. Arrangements of bids in collusion with unions have been observed in many cities in the construction field and sometimes in job printing businesses. These
tend to have the effect of preserving the current market structure
where it is oligopolistically organized.[17]
    At the other end of the structural picture we find influence on

---

[16] Fritz Machlup, "Monopolistic Wage Determination as a Part of the General
Problem of Monopoly," First 1947 Economic Institute (Proceedings), Wage Determi-
nation and Economics of Liberalism, Chamber of Commerce of the United States,
Washington, D. C., January 11, 1947, (p. 62).
    [17] Pollak, op. cit., p. 57.

market structures in the commendable efforts of many unions to preserve small companies in the highly competitive clothing business of New York's 7th Avenue.

Market structure is sometimes affected by unions when they first organize a plant. Usually firms exhibit a highly emotional reaction to unions, when a union first enters the picture. Unionism is a traumatic and anxiety-producing experience to the managers or owners of a newly organized plant. The temptation of the company is to treat the workers as ungrateful, and to attempt to avoid the indignities and restrictions of the relationship that they fear collective bargaining will usher in. Some older owners, some highly emotional owners, and some marginal owners sell out and quit the business. It is a standing joke that some union organizers have a drawer full of keys to plants offered to them by frustrated owners of newly organized plants. Of course, it is well for such owners to keep duplicate keys, because there are probably very few companies which actually do make good their threat of going out of business at the inception of the collective bargaining relationship. But they do from time to time. Within three years in the early 1960's, a large number of machine tool shops in central New York voluntarily went out of business soon after they were first organized. This extreme reaction occurs sometimes even after unionization has continued in the plant for a period of time. Such cases, however, seem to be very rare.

I think it is safe to conclude that in spite of the situations I have reported (and undoubtedly some others), labor unions have only a minimal effect upon market structure.

INDUSTRY EFFICIENCY

Any discussion of industry efficiency must draw substantially upon the expertise of the economist and engineer. Since I am neither, my emphasis will be on attitudes and aims of unions. Even in this restricted area, my statements must be viewed as mostly impressionistic and episodic.

The general view is that union organization tends to diminish industrial efficiency, rather than to improve it.[18] There is no need to recite here the restrictions on production in certain parts of the construction industry. Refusal to work on materials produced in another shop is often found in building trade union practices; reassembly of electrical products is often required by electrical unions. We are familiar with full crew laws on the

[18]G. F. Bloom and H. R. Northrup, Economics of Labor and Industrial Relations, Blakiston, Philadelphia, 1950, p. 489.

railroads, or the equivalent among workers in the building trades, and among truck drivers and longshoremen. Nor does it seem necessary to recount that in the most respectable of union contracts there are provisions for seniority, production standards, apprenticeship regulations, hours of work and their scheduling, subcontracting of work and other protective devices and restrictions. All of them may be sufficiently desirable from labor's view, but they are certainly not efficient, at least in the short run, from the standpoint of the employer of labor. The whole tendency is to prevent the employer from eliminating costly operations and introducing improved methods of production. Sincere economists, friendly to labor, have little hope in the present state of things for unions to take a strong interest in efficiency, except in isolated cases, principally where it is necessary to bail out a marginal firm having difficulty in meeting the union scale[19] or when a whole industry is in a depressed state.[20] Many economists feel that union wage pressure may afford stimulus to technological progress in its broader aspects; so have some union officials, one of whom has stated:

In a dynamic industrial society, such as we have in the United States, wage increases and high labor rates have served as an additional important stimulus to high productivity. The prevalence of interproduct competition and the actual conflict over markets have meant that wage increases have quickened methods of production. The very determination by unions to seek higher wages has also been encouraged by the experience that such increases have been compensated by managerial improvements. The success of one wage movement and managerial achievements in offsetting its impact on costs through labor-saving innovations has fed additional efforts in the same direction. In combination with other economic influences they have fostered more highly capitalized production methods and advanced products and services with lower labor content.[21]

Some, however, including Bloom and Northrup, doubt whether general union wage adjustments occurring more or less simultaneously over a broad area of industry will provide much stimulation to the rate of mechanization. They feel that whatever stimulus is forthcoming will tend to be offset by the restrictive influence of union policies which retard the rate of introduction of labor-saving machinery.[22]

[19]L. G. Reynolds, Labor Economics and Labor Relations, Prentice-Hall, New York, 1949, p. 439.
[20]Joseph Shister, "Union-Management Cooperation: An Analysis," in R. A. Lester and Joseph Shister, editors, Insights Into Labor Issues, The Macmillan Company, New York, 1948, pp. 87-115.
[21]Solomon Barkin, "Trade Union Attitudes and Their Effect Upon Productivity," in Solomon Barkin et al.; editors, Industrial Productivity, Industrial Relations Research Association, December 1951.
[22]G. F. Bloom and H. R. Northrup, op. cit., p. 489.

Organized labor, as a general rule, does not officially attack the introduction of labor-saving devices or automation.[23] The leaders are well informed as to the long-run advantages. But it is understandable that even the most responsible of them must have a greater preoccupation with the short-run.[24] Their national concern and their concern in every industry is with unemployment, dislocation, layoffs, distressed communities and regions, destruction of traditional job classifications, downgrading workers — to say nothing of the effect upon the demand for the products manufactured. Unions thus demand and have gained an increasing voice in the introduction of automation; the very least they demand is advance notice and joint consultation. The National Labor Relations Board, in cases of extreme importance, has indicated a willingness to give in more and more to these aspirations.[25]

This whole problem is one of vast size and many facets. In the face of it all, I think I had better go back to my original impression that union organization in and of itself, either for good reasons or bad, tends to diminish industrial efficiency. I realize, of course, that this is mostly surmise. It will probably remain so. Especially difficult to measure is the amount of stimulation to technological progress caused by union wage pressure. The resistance of the unions to technological progress is easy to detail, but the effectiveness of this resistance in any industry is hard to measure. The food industry seems to be no exception.

Perhaps in closing I should make a brief comment on two situations in the food industry that illustrate the unions' attitude toward efficiency and a possible relationship to the other subject of this chapter, market structure. I have been personally involved in the movement among the New York milk marketing cooperatives to buy million-dollar plants for the processing of surplus milk into such products as powder and butter. The atmosphere of this whole movement was enthusiastic; this derived not so much from the economics of disposal of surplus milk by these plants, but rather from the thrill of being associated with such an efficient plant and process. In all the discussions regarding these new plants, the union problem clearly revealed itself to be minor. To tell the truth, there were going to be very few laborers hired and the assumption seemed to be that whether they were organized or not, the wages of the workers would be digestible by the plants.

---

[23] Nat Goldfinger, Department of Research AFL-CIO, "Labor Looks at Automation," Conference on Automation, University of California, January 9, 1957, p. 12.

[24] Goldfinger, op. cit., pp. 13-17.

[25] Town and Country Manufacturing Company, Inc. and Town and Country Sales Co., Inc., and General Drivers, Chauffeurs & Helpers Local Union No. 886, 136 NLRB 111, April 13, 1962; Carl Rochet et al. d/b/a Renton News Record et al. and Seattle Typographical Union No. 202, AFL-CIO, 136 NLRB 55, April 24, 1962.

Simultaneously, I was concerned with the attempt of the large baking companies in central New York to transform their operations from the traditional methods to modern automation. (Some small bakeries closed; whether in whole or in part, caused by union wage pressure, no one can know.) Here the problems of the union pervade all phases of the modernization — problems of notice to the union, consultation with the union, procuring the consent of the union to do the installation of the process, setting wage rates for the new jobs, taking care of the displaced workers, problems of retraining and "red circling" (preserving) of rates for downgraded workers, and lengthy and costly arbitrations over the subject of combining of jobs or the complement of workers to be assigned a certain job. These matters taxed the nerves and ingenuity of management and can be fairly counted as substantial additional costs to the bakeries that the cooperatives with their new milk plants do not have to face at the outset.

There may be a large and growing number of situations where labor attitudes and practices toward efficiency give new firms an especially gentle ease of entry into a field where they have enough capital to command the latest technical processes and machinery and have the full freedom to install them before the union can organize the firm. If this is true, then the unions' attitude toward efficiency must be seen to have an effect on market structure, though an effect unintended by them.

The greatest effect of unionism upon market structure may very well be in the area of the growing union control over plant efficiency. The consequences may be dramatic, sometimes completely unintended by the union, and often most important to the survival of firms in the industry, their growth and the entry of new firms.

In conclusion, I would like to point out that since this chapter is of an overview nature, I have not dealt basically with any phase of research in this field. The amount of research in the general field of labor relations has been extremely impressive. In 1948, in the American Economic Association's Survey of Contemporary Economics, there was an extensive summary of the contributions to knowledge in the field of labor economics since the early 1930's. Since that time the Industrial Relations Research Association has carried on their job by publishing A Decade of Industrial Relations Research 1946 - 1956, and Employment Relations Research, A Summary and Appraisal (1960). A good source for information on industrial relations research is the "News and Notes" department of the Industrial and Labor Relations Review, Ithaca, New York. Appearing in each quarterly issue of the Review, "News and Notes" consists of reports from the research institutes of various universities on work done and work in progress.

PART THREE

OPERATIONAL CRITERIA

Chapter 5

ROBERT L. CLODIUS

University of Wisconsin

Operational criteria for public programs affecting firm entry and exit

T HIS TOPIC logically divides itself into three parts. One deals with entry and exit, the concepts and their measurement. The second deals with public programs and policies, and the third with operational criteria. Each part might well be given extended treatment beyond the scope of this chapter, but I shall try to give some consideration to each.

ENTRY

The definitions of entry and exit are special, perhaps moot, involve ownership and are rooted even more fundamentally in the concept of capacity. An increase in capacity is a necessary condition for entry. Because capacity might be increased either by internal growth of a firm or by a new firm, entry may be specified as new capacity in a firm representing ownership that is new to the industry. Actual or realized entry and exit would necessarily be reflected in the number of firms in an industry and could be subsumed under the structural heading of numbers. However, because actual numbers of firms do not reflect potential numbers of firms, specific consideration must be given to entry and exit.

There is analytical usefulness in such a definition of entry and exit. Just as there are the income effect and the substitution effect of a price change in price theory, there are the "capacity effect" and the "numbers effect" of a change in firm entry or exit. In an industry where scale is significant, the capacity effect of entry would be great. Or in an industry of few firms, the numbers effect of entry might be very important. The significance of the capacity effect and the numbers effect of entry will be apparent later.

Entry, or the threat of entry, and its opposite number, exit, fill a strategic spot in current theory explaining predicted or

observed overt economic behavior of firms and industries. In
normative models the ultimate public good is served or denied as
firms either do or do not enter and leave.

The standard reference on entry as a structural element is
Joseph S. Bain, Barriers to New Competition.[1] In fact, because
of it, this chapter must be, in part, a review of Bain.[2] What did
Bain say about entry and exit, and where do we go from here?
The condition of entry is evaluated roughly "by the advantages of
established sellers in an industry over potential entrant sellers,
these advantages being reflected in the extent to which established
sellers can persistently raise their prices above a competitive
level without attracting new firms to enter the industry."[3] It
"may be measured on a numerical scale ... as the largest percentage by which established sellers can persistently elevate
their prices above the minimized or competitive average costs
of production and distribution (plus average cost of sales promotion) without inducing new sellers to enter the industry."[4]

Barriers to Entry

The "barriers" to entry fall into three categories. They are
the absolute cost advantage to established firms, product differentiation advantages to established firms and scale advantages to
established firms.

Absolute cost advantages may be found in the control of superior production techniques by patents or secrecy, in monopolization of resources, in limitations on supplies of necessary factors
or in more favorable conditions in the money market for established firms. Product differentiation advantages include the ac-
cumulated preferences of buyers for established brand names
and company reputations, control of superior product design or
quality, or favored systems of distribution or outlets by established firms. Scale advantages of established firms are important
if the output at the optimum scale is a significant part of industry
output.

Bain attempts to determine the existence of these three sorts
of barriers to entry in each of twenty industries and to measure
the height of the barrier. Industries having some direct relevance

[1] J. S. Bain, Barriers to New Competition, Harvard University Press,
Cambridge, 1956.
[2] Including J. S. Bain, Industrial Organization, John Wiley & Sons, Inc.,
New York, 1959.
[3] Bain, Barriers to New Competition, p. 3.
[4] Bain, Industrial Organization, p. 237.

to agriculture included meat packing, canned fruits and vegetables, flour milling, cigarettes and farm machinery. Using ordinally significant classifications such as "very important," "moderately important," "important," "relatively unimportant," "great," "very large," "large," "moderate," "slight" and "small," he rates each industry with respect to its barriers to entry.

In a final ranking of aggregate barrier to entry he places the agriculturally related industries as follows: Very high entry barrier — cigarettes; substantial entry barrier — farm machines (large, complex); moderate to low entry barrier — farm machinery (small, simple); flour, canned fruits and vegetables, and meat packing. He notes further that flour, canned fruits and vegetables, and meat packing in many major segments lie at the "low" end of the "low entry" barrier.[5] Presumably the cigarette industry can elevate price by 10 percent or more above minimal average costs without inducing entry. In the industry of large, complex farm machinery, prices might be elevated 5 to 8 percent above minimal average costs without inducing entry. In flour, canned fruits and vegetables, and meat packing, the maximum excess of price over cost could not exceed 4 percent and might be more like 1 or 2 percent.

Of course, opinions of this work will differ. To me, it seems to promise more than it actually delivers in terms of research results. Also, there is a spurious accuracy in stating that the height of the barrier may be measured on a numerical scale at the percentage that price may be persistently elevated above costs, etc., when the entire analysis is based on judgments about "very large," "very high," "important," "substantial," "moderate," and "slight" or "low." The quality of the work turns on the quality of the judgments made by the author. Fortunately, Joe Bain is a skilled and articulate craftsman in the industrial organization field.

The point to be made here is that the skill of the economist in the market structure field is making informed judgments. Judgment enters in the choice of the initial problems, the selection of factors to be probed, the techniques of measurement employed, the determination of the aggregative effect on the barrier, and finally the policy implications to be drawn. Presumably the more skillful the economist the better the judgments; thus it follows that not everyone should be engaged in market structure research. It also follows that there will likely be some variations in research results. Research "solutions" will probably represent a consensus among people in the field rather than proof in the formal scientific sense.

---

[5] Bain, Barriers to New Competition, pp. 168-70.

Bain has provided agricultural economists a basis for investigating various barriers to entry in a systematic way. An absolute cost advantage would be anything causing a potential entrant to use an inferior production technique or to pay higher prices for factors. This leads to investigation of such things as patents or firm secrets or "know-how" unavailable to an entrant. Estimates could be made of the cost to the entrant of using "second-best" methods. Each of the factor markets could be investigated to see if there were limitations on either the price or availability of supplies, labor, materials and money capital.

Similarly, research attention could be directed at the scale economies of established firms and product differentiation barriers. Agricultural economists are familiar with research on scale of firms in many agricultural markets. This and new research could be oriented to the entry dimension.

Our general uneasiness and periodic interest about advertising expenditures in agricultural markets now take a specific focus. They are part of broader questions about product differentiation both as a structural variable in its own right and as one of the elements of the condition of entry. Buyers develop preferences for brand names and company reputations whether based on experience or ignorance. Advertising reinforces these preferences. Established sellers may also have developed large dealer or service organizations. This is a kind of vertical integration that is important in its own right, but also as a barrier to any potential entrant.

Sometimes sellers develop exclusive control of superior product designs or quality. Advertising conveys certain information here and on a continuing basis reinforces buyers' preferences. Underlying this externally evidenced barrier is a more fundamental one of research and development expenditures. R and D has proven to be a dynamic force in many industries and has now been built into the operations of established firms.

Research and development as a barrier to entry has been mentioned here as it relates to product differentiation. However, it functions with equal force in the absolute cost advantages and the scale economies categories of barriers. It seems to me this is one of the important elements overlooked by Bain.

It seems likely to me that investigation of barriers in a specific industry might reveal one or two "strategic" elements of significance such as patents were revealed to be in Nicholls' study of cheese[6] or as arbitrary trade barriers are to entry in

---

[6] W. H. Nicholls, Post-War Developments in the Marketing of Cheese, Iowa Agricultural Experiment Station Research Bulletin 261, 1939.

certain spatial markets. Within the product differentiation barrier examples might be the Borden name itself or the system of
dealer outlets and service stores that appear to be critical in the
automobile industry, as Mr. Kaiser discovered.

There are formidable problems in trying to measure these
barriers. They might be investigated in several categories and
aggregated on a judgmental basis as Bain has done or they might
be approached from the aggregate directly as Mueller and Garoian
have done. They based their estimates on the smallest-sized,
actual, recent entrant. With impeccable logic they argue that
firms of the same type but larger than actual entrants must be
viewed as potential entrants. [7]

Other operational measures may be made that relate to entry.
Profit ratios mask the specific source of profit but might be related to absolute cost barriers such as patents or resource monopolization. Advertising expenditures and computed ratios relate
to product differentiation barriers and perhaps to the sales promotion advantages of established firms. Research and development expenditures and their ratios may be indications of both
absolute cost and product differentiation barriers. Measures of
the cost-volume relationship relate to scale barriers.

Finally there are various measures of seller concentration.
While firm numbers and size do not reveal potential entry, they
are ex post facto results of entry. Well-known measures are
concentration ratios of the Big 4, the Big 8, or the largest 20.
Concentration of ownership of assets may also have significance,
as well as the concentration of plants.

I would like to see someone play around with the "synthetic"
method for empirical measurement of entry. Economists optimize all kinds of situations. Agricultural economists have been
particularly active in synthesizing optimum farms, dairy plants,
fruit and vegetable packing and processing plants, and even geographical regions. Could we synthesize an optimum entrant into
some agriculturally related industry? Its characteristics would
be measures of the heights of barriers from at least one point of
view.

EXIT

Exit is a concept still largely to be defined and an area to be
examined empirically. As a first approximation one may think of

---

[7] W. F. Mueller and L. Garoian, The Changing Market Structure of Grocery
Retailing, University of Wisconsin Press, Madison, 1961.

it as simple, negative entry. It could be evaluated as the advantage present sellers have over the potential egressor and could be measured as the largest percentage by which price could fall relative to minimized average costs without inducing an existing firm with its capacity to leave the industry. Continuing the negative analogy would establish zero barriers to exit as (1) absolute cost disadvantages, (2) scale diseconomies and (3) product disadvantages. If established firms had absolute cost advantages, scale economies and product differentiation advantages, presumably barriers to exit are high, and price would have to fall far below minimized cost to force firms out.

Perhaps exit requires something different from negative parallellism with respect to entry. To date entry has been considered on one side only — the intra-industry inducements to entry and the barriers thereto. The factors on the side of availability and the push of ownership and assets into the industry from extra-industry sources have been assumed constant. In exit problems one is struck by the fact there are both push and pull factors at work and that exit is relative to them both. All this can be expressed within a familiar framework (Figure 5.1).

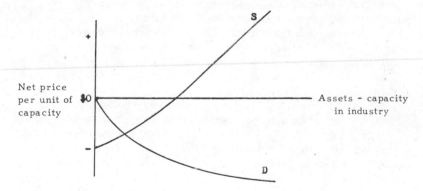

Figure 5.1. The Supply and Demand for Assets — Capacity of Established Firms in an Industry for Use Outside the Industry.

The curve D represents the alternative net prices (salvage price minus book value per unit of capacity) that buyers would be willing to pay for potential exiting capacity. It is a demand curve of outside buyers for old assets representing capacity leaving an industry. Curve S represents the amounts of assets-capacity that would be offered by exiting firms at alternative prices. Exit is realized where offers to sell and offers to buy are equal, and here the price (or cost) of exit is determined.

Barriers to Exit

Barriers to exit as the negative of an entry are found on the supply side. Two major assumptions underlie the position of the supply curve. It takes as given (1) the price of the product (AR) at some level relative to minimized average cost determining a negative or a positive net income and (2) the height of the barriers to exit. Both determine the degree of "push" of capacity out of the industry. If product price falls so that firms suffer greater operating losses, the supply curve shifts to the right, indicating that for every net price of exiting capacity a greater amount of it will be offered. Similarly, a decrease in barriers to exit shifts the curve to the right and more capacity would be offered for exit at every net price.

The demand for old assets is related to their net productivity in the next best alternative use. Net productivity is specified because there may be costs in converting assets from old to new uses. Here, some notion of the elasticity of substitution or marginal rates of substitution would be useful. It could be applied to both assets and management and should consider machinery, equipment, building, land, location, good will, accounts, brand names, trade marks, etc. It should be obvious that the closer the firm is to complete liquidity or the more easily it can be made liquid, the greater the demand. A shift of demand would also be related to changes in the productivity of these assets.

This kind of a framework for considering exit has real potential for empirical measurement and research. Firms in industries could be examined to determine their degree of liquidity; hence, flexibility in moving. Analysis of the debt structure would show the magnitude of debt, length of lending period and type of debt. Undistributed dividends and cash reserves would be important, as well as the magnitude of depreciation reserves and the stage of life of the plant and equipment. Realistic appraisals could be made of the value of buildings, warehouses, and good will, brand names and trademarks.

On the supply side of exit, calculations could be made of the various operating ratios for firms that had recently egressed. Certain values might be regarded as indicators of potential egressors. The losses associated with actual exit would be a measure of the aggregate barrier. This kind of empirical study of exit was under way on a cooperative basis in 1962 between the Economic Research Service and the University of Wisconsin.

PUBLIC POLICIES AND PROGRAMS

Establishing the operational rules or tests by which entry and exit are tried in forming a correct judgment cannot be considered apart from public policies regarding a competitive behavior and the programs to implement those policies.

First, a few comments about public policy generally are in order. Economists are divided in the logic of their approach to policy. Some set up arbitrary goals that they conceive to be important, establish criteria of performance in relation to these goals and judge policy and programs accordingly. Variously, they use efficiency, income distribution, stability and growth as criteria. Policies to optimize with respect to each are stated to be "good," and so saying, the economist exhibits an immodestly superior, infinite and very conventional wisdom.

The second view is one that seems well suited to the industrial organization field. It is completely pragmatic. Policy arises because there are problems that affect groups of people and that cannot be solved by individual action. Policy is what emerges as a generally accepted course of action to be administered and enforced by recognized authority. The implementation of the agreed-upon policy is the program. It involves the specification of definitions, rules, regulations and procedures whereby the authorities can execute the policy. It is judged by criteria which involve the success of the program in implementing the policy and solving the problem.

In the context of industrial organization, programs are those activities carried on by the Antitrust Division of the U. S. Department of Justice and by the Federal Trade Commission at the federal level. They are executing policies defined by Congress and the courts. The critical question is: What problems produced these policies? Only in terms of the original problems and of present problems are the criteria established for a true evaluation of public policies and programs with respect to competition.

This is a good place, but space does not permit a full discussion of competitive problems a century ago and continuing. Mention of the Granger Movement and the "robber barons" should be sufficient to conjure an image of a rampant capitalism with the public to be damned and anyone else who got in the way. The response to these experienced problems was public policy embodied in the Sherman Act. Following more experienced problems in the administration of this act and to remedy its shortcoming, the Clayton Act and Federal Trade Commission Act came in 1914. The early 1930's saw problems of depression that were not

generally understood. But small businessmen experienced se-
vere difficulties, many of which were attributed to unreasonable
advantages of their large competitors. It is small wonder that
the Robinson-Patman Act was passed in 1936.

Thinking about policy and programs in terms of response to
experienced problems may be a departure for many academic
economists, but I believe it is essentially the way that legislators,
politicians and lawyers view these things. Anyway, it is necessary to pursue both points of view as they bear on the specification of operational criteria for public programs.

Another worthwhile observation about public programs is that
they will be effective only as dependable relationships have been
found between the variable being manipulated and the outcome
sought. This is a job for research in market structure — the testing of relationships between structure, conduct and performance.
In the specific instance it is the relationship between entry and
exit, and conduct and performance. Generally high barriers to
entry are believed to be associated with undesirable performance.
So much depends upon the level of other features of structure,
however. In industries of large numbers and differentiated products characterized in classical Chamberlinian monopolistic competition, completely easy entry often produces chaotic conditions
of chronic surplus capacity, frequent price wars, and high rates
of bankruptcy and business turnover. Can anyone argue that
these are desirable social results? Also, in oligopolistic markets Bain writes of markets where barriers are low and oligopolistic pricing patterns prevail. They are likely to lead to chronic
instability of market structure, to wastes of excess capacity and
to wide variations in output and price.[8] With qualifications he
sees this as a possible outcome in miller's-brand consumer
flour, meat packing, standard canned goods and commercial flour.[9]

The inescapable conclusion is that we do not now know reliable and predictable relationships between the condition of entry
and market performance. In one sense, therefore, it is idle and
misleading to formulate either operational criteria or public
programs concerning entry and exit. But when have economists
ever allowed lack of knowledge to stand in the way of prescriptions for public policy!

---

[8] Bain, Barriers to New Competition, p. 41.
[9] Ibid, pp. 178-79.

FROM THEORETICAL CRITERIA TO PROGRAMS

If it can be concluded that the public interest is served by a general reduction of barriers, theoretical considerations based on conventional criteria of efficiency, stability, etc., suggest certain programs. Each item turned up in the theoretical analysis can be checked off for its program implications.

Absolute cost advantages of established firms would be attacked in several ways. Where patent rights are administered to prevent entry, laws might be changed and action instituted through the courts to minimize their effects. Length of life of patents might be decreased to reduce the lag in potential entry. Resource monopolization through integration would be attacked by requiring disintegration. However, if such disintegration would reduce efficiency in production or in finding and developing new resources, it would not be ordered.[10]

Minimizing the effects of the capital requirements to entry is a hazardous program. Some look to the capital available to large firms in other industries, and see such firms as vaulters of the capital barrier. This they may be and entry might even be accomplished, but it fails to consider the structural effect of entry where the degree of vertical integration might be increased. A highly integrated firm entering another industry is more than just another seller, as Mueller and I have argued elsewhere.[11]

Barriers based on scale economies are also hard to deal with. If the economies are genuine and social, they should be maintained on efficiency grounds. Sales-promotional advantages of scale are suspect unless real economies exist, and programs to reduce the barrier are indicated. Disintegration and breakup, though difficult, seem to offer the most possibilities.

It is easy for the economist to become indignant over the product-differentiation barrier to entry. Indicated programs are a tax on advertising or not allowing it as a cost. Wide-scale public information programs, compulsory truthful labeling, compulsory grading according to publicly defined standards are other examples of programs in pursuit of the policy of reducing barriers to entry.

In agriculture and in many agricultural marketing industries, favoring exit may be more appropriate than entry in the public interest, except as reducing entry barriers makes it easier for firms to exit. These factors look only to the "push" side of exit,

---

[10] Ibid, p. 215.

[11] R. L. Clodius and W. F. Mueller, "Market Structure Analysis as an Orientation for Research in Agricultural Economics," Journal of Farm Economics, August 1961, pp. 519-20.

whereas the "pull" side might be just as important as our earlier theoretical model suggests. An active market for potentially egressing assets may be difficult to work out in a public program. Some have argued that land resources which originally came from the public domain might be purchased by a government agency and returned again to the public domain. The Soil Bank produced some kind of a market alternative for land, but cannot be regarded as true exit since only capacity was reduced but entrepreneurs were not eased out except indirectly. "Homesteads in reverse" is an idea directed to true exit.

Programs directed at pulling out the entrepreneurial element only are suspect because they consider the numbers effect of exit and not the capacity effect. In other words, programs to train farmers, supply them credit, etc., to leave agriculture is not true exit. Because of the large numbers already in agriculture, the numbers effect of such departures is not likely to bring about a structural change of significance and since there will be no capacity reduction effect, the performance of agriculture is likely to continue to be unsatisfactory.

As for the agricultural processing industries, what can be done to facilitate the exit of both entrepreneurs and capacity where such exit is indicated in the public interest? If the experience in the state of Wisconsin is typical, there is surplus productive capacity in both the dairy processing and pea and corn canning industries.

FROM PROBLEM CRITERIA TO PROGRAMS

A second approach to policy and public programs begins with a consideration of the genuine problems that confront society in matters of market behavior. I read them as problems of (1) economic power, (2) growth and (3) distribution of opportunity and income. Public programs bearing on entry-exit alone contribute a little bit. Programs dealing with market structures in general contribute a great deal more, but perhaps not enough.

Exercise of economic power as a social problem was demonstrated most vividly in April, 1962, when U. S. Steel announced a price increase of $6 per ton and was dutifully followed almost immediately by five other major producers, but was rescinded only after the President of the United States got into the act. The administering of prices and profiteering among industrial producers are equalled only by the cost-push of unions for ever more in their exercise of economic power. The business community's philosophy was stated nakedly and approvingly by Time

as "to applaud Roger Blough's dramatic affirmation of the right of
a businessman in a democratic, free-enterprise society to set his
own prices."[12] Nor have I read where any labor leader has dis-
avowed Adolph Strasser's one-word classic statement of the direction of union wage and benefits policy: "More."

There are several criteria for public programs to meet this
problem, but I shall suggest only one. It is size. In 1960 the 500
largest industrials had sales of $204.7 billion. These represented
57 percent of the sales of all industrials and 72 percent of the
profits. It provides an opportunity for a relatively tiny handful
of executives in pursuit of private power and profit to show utter
contempt for the interest of 185 million Americans — to borrow
from the President's press statement about the steel price increase. Does this suggest some kind of absolute criterion that
entry of any kind by one of the 500 be prohibited whether vertical,
horizontal or conglomerate? Does it suggest that whenever
growth, whether internal or by merger, reaches a certain size
that the corporation be required to "spin off" assets and set up
separate and independent firms in a form of "compulsory" entry?
Specifically the corporations involved are examples like Swift,
Armour, National Dairy, General Foods, Corn Products Refining,
Wilson, General Mills, Campbell Soup, John Morrell, Ralston
Purina, National Biscuit, Beatrice Foods, Standard Brands, Fore-
most Dairies, Carnation, Hygrade Food Products, Continental
Baking, Pillsbury, George Hormel, California Packing, Cudahy,
H. J. Heinz, Hunt Foods & Industries, Quaker Oats, and so on.[13]

There is no such convenient listing of union size, but does it
not seem reasonable there is some absolute size beyond which
the Teamsters should not be allowed to grow?

In terms of the problem of growth of the economy as a whole
and using a desirable rate of growth as the criterion, what are
appropriate public programs? The administration seems to be
relying strongly on accelerated depreciation write-offs and tax
credits for modernization. The first may act to reduce barriers
to entry if appropriately applied, but it appears generally these
proposals foster expansion of existing firms and ignore structure.
So little is known about the optimum structures for economic development and growth that even speculating about an entry-exit
program would be idle. Schumpeter's suggestion that monopoly
fosters innovation and Adam Smith's implied atomistic structures
for enhancing the wealth of nations are polar alternatives that create
great uncertainty and leave the middle a kind of "no man's land."

---

[12] Time, The Weekly Newsmagazine, April 20, 1962, pp. 89-90.
[13] Fortune Magazine, July 1961.

The distribution of opportunity and income associated with the organization of industry are continuing social problems. Both political and economic democracy rely on their being broadly distributed without great inequities, and these constitute criteria for judging public programs. My belief is that these kinds of problems must be attacked operationally at their margins. It is quite well established that most industries are characterized by a "competitive fringe" of some sort. These are small businesses relative to the concentrated few, and often it is the market behavior of the fringe that maintains any semblance of reasonably effective competition in aggregative performance. Furthermore it would seem that small business represents a broad basis of opportunity. These criteria suggest support of public programs to encourage small business in specific circumstances.

Farming's problems of low income and inadequate opportunities are familiar to all. For farmers as well as for their resources it is a question of alternatives. Using the enhancement of alternatives as a criterion suggests several programs of which some have already been considered as matters of exit — both push and pull. Using enhancement of income as a criterion suggests structurally oriented programs that involve supply control where the decision on output is shifted from an atomistic structure to an administrative structure that is nonatomistic.

In summary there appear to be two sets of criteria for judging public programs affecting market structures. Specifically they are entry and exit. To some extent they overlap. Out of pure theory come criteria of efficiency, income distribution, price and income stability and progress. My personal judgment of the problems of our day in the industrial organization field brought forth criteria of control of economic power, growth and distribution of opportunity as well as income. The pure approach lends itself to taking one structural variable, such as the condition of entry, and systematically deducing its policy implications. The problem orientation lends itself to taking whatever factor that judgment suggests might be important and trying it on for size in combination with anything else that might be appropriate. It remains to be seen which approach is most suitable for public programs.

Let me conclude by tossing in a couple of questions and comments that stick in my own mind as ones that seem especially important. Is there economic significance in trying to distinguish exit as being something beyond a mere consideration of a general condition of entry? If so, the concept of exit certainly needs further theoretical consideration. In addition, it opens a wide field of research relating barriers to exit and market performance. Only by a thorough understanding of these relationships may we recommend public policy with respect to barriers to exit as being in the public interest.

Finally, the orientation of this chapter has been primarily inter-industry. Entry, exit and public policy have been considered across industry lines as though one were considering representative conditions of one industry with those of other industries. However, most industrial organization problems arise within or specific to an industry rather than across industries. It may be agriculture or it may be steel that is performing badly. As price is elevated or depressed, we question what firms in particular will be potential and/or actual entrants and egressors. What are their characteristics? Who will leave first and who will enter first? In my judgment here is the strategic area for theory and empirical research that will have the utmost significance for public programs in fact.

HARRISON F. HOUGHTON
U.S. House of Representatives

DISCUSSION

I T IS NOW a generation since Chamberlin[1] and Joan Robinson[2] in 1933 were in a photofinish race to announce that the real world consists largely of oligopolies, and that pure or perfect competition, to which monopoly was an occasional aberration, no longer was a worthy symbol of reality. Despite the high stakes involved, Mrs. Robinson paused long enough to offer a word of advice to the tool makers in economic analysis. "The gap between the tool makers and the tool users is a distressingly wide one," she said, "and no economist can fail to have sympathy with the impatience of the politician, the businessman, and the statistical investigator, who complain of the extremely poor, arid, or even misleading information with which the analytical economists provide him."[3]

This advice seems most pertinent as we explore the question of entry and market structure, particularly in relation to public policy.

---

[1] Edward Chamberlin, The Theory of Monopolistic Competition, Harvard University Press, 1933.
[2] Joan Robinson, The Economics of Imperfect Competition, The Macmillan Co., 1933.
[3] Ibid, p. 1.

EMPHASIS ON ENTRY: A RECENT DEVELOPMENT

Emphasis on entry, both in the theoretical literature and in public policy, seems to be of relatively recent origin. The august Encyclopedia of the Social Sciences,[4] for example, does not include the term "entry." The subject is not specially treated in Handler's[5] TNEC monograph on the antitrust laws, and is only briefly discussed in Wilcox's[6] monograph on competition and monopoly in American industry. The legislative history of the Celler-Kefauver Anti-Merger Act is silent on the question. Yet entry has become an issue in a number of merger cases under that act, is the subject of a major study by one of our leading academic economists, and is now a matter before this symposium.

Mr. Clodius' stimulating paper contains a most intriguing suggestion: namely, that a barrier to entry to the field of market structure research should be erected. Restricting the field to the more skillful economists capable of "informed judgments," he says, will probably yield "a consensus among people in the field rather than proof in the formal scientific sense."[7]

But when even the most thorough statistical studies must clear the hearsay rule before becoming probative, one may question seriously whether "informed judgments" can be too useful to the policy maker. Skill and judgment are not perfect substitutes for facts.

Aside from this, a broader question arises as to whether the language, definitions and techniques used by the market structure tool maker are suitable for shaping public policy. Antitrust enforcement is concerned with certain concepts, more legal than economic. For example, the keystone of monopolization is summed up in the phrase "power over price or power to exclude." The antimerger statute (Section 7 of the Clayton Act) deals with incipient monopoly. The academic market structure specialist is concerned with the relation between market structure and performance, and with workable competition. Neither of these concepts incorporates standards universally agreed upon by economists. While the theorist may provide very provocative propositions in regard to entry, the question arises as to how applicable they are, either to present antitrust enforcement or new legislation.

[4] Encyclopedia of the Social Sciences, The Macmillan Co., 1930.
[5] Milton Handler, A Study of the Construction and Enforcement of the Antitrust Laws, TNEC Monograph No. 38, 1941.
[6] Clair Wilcox, Competition and Monopoly in American Industry, TNEC Monograph No. 21, 1940.
[7] R. L. Clodius, Operational Criteria for Public Programs Affecting Firm Entry and Exit. This book.

Celler-Kefauver Act

The thrust of the Celler-Kefauver Act is primarily structural.
The legislative mandate, reflected in the government's presentation in litigated cases, is that the key question in a merger is the
impact on concentration. The first mention of entry appears to
have occurred in the Federal Trade Commission remand in the
Pillsbury case,[8] where the Commission insisted that "all relevant
factors" must be considered, including the pattern of acquisitions
in the industry, the general increase in market shares, a decline
in the number of mills, a lack of new entries and a movement in
the direction of oligopoly in particular markets. The door left
ajar for entry by Pillsbury was opened wide by the Attorney General's National Committee To Study the Antitrust Laws, which
devoted an entire section to the matter.[9]

If defendants took heart by this introduction of entry as a
factor of significance, their enthusiasm should not have led to
hilarity, for the entry picture has influenced decisions to veto
mergers, rather than to approve them. In Crystal Sugar, an early
private case, the district court observed that "amelioration of
market structure conditions" was unlikely through reasonable
access to the industry by new entrants.[10]

In Bethlehem,[11] the first government case decided by the
courts, the lack of entry over a long historical period reinforced
the court's conclusion as to the merger's prospective bad effects.
The court commented as follows (at 606-7):

The prospect of a new entrant to replace an absorbed Youngstown,
either in terms of capital investment or experience, is in the light of the
history of this industry, practically nihil....
The new entrants have made no real dent as far as the larger integrated companies are concerned.... The evidence establishes that the industry is and will be frozen in the foreseeable future into the present
number of integrated steel producers.

Defendants had not disputed the government's showing of extreme difficulty of entry of fully integrated steel companies, but
had urged that vigorous competition was encouraged by other
forms of entry, such as backward integration by semi- or non-
integrated firms, or by steel consumers. "Still other kinds of
entry are economically important," argued defendants' final

[8] FTC Docket 6000 (1953).
[9] Report of the Attorney General's National Committee To Study the Antitrust
Laws, March 31, 1955, pp. 326-27.
[10] American Crystal Sugar Co. v. The Cuban-American Sugar Co., 152 F. Supp.
387, 400 (S.D. N.Y. 1957).
[11] U.S. v. Bethlehem, 168 F. Supp. 576 (S.D. N.Y. 1958).

brief, including penetration into new regions, expansion of certain producers at rates exceeding those of its rivals and vertical expansions providing "a form of immediately available entry which necessarily places formidable obstacles in the path of any steel producer attempting to exercise restraints over price and other competitive standards with respect to a particular finished steel product."[12] Apparently these arguments were not decisively impressive to the court.

An interesting sidelight on the question of entry in the Bethlehem case revolved around the item Track Spikes — one of the lines of commerce. The government demonstrated negligible entry over a long span of years in the production of this item. Defendants argued, nonetheless, that cost of entry is slight and that consuming railroads could easily acquire spike-making machines and thus prevent any enhancement of prices.[13] The court disregarded this argument, which if carried to its ultimate implications, would have involved examination of many peripheral questions, such as reciprocity, the price such railroads would have to pay for the raw material, bar steel, etc., etc.

Bok[14] has carefully examined the Brillo proceeding before the FTC with respect to the relevance of entry, and comments:

> With respect to new entry... practically no attention was paid to the question of precisely why this issue should be involved at all. Apparently, the assumption was made that any merger in a market where entry is comparatively easy would be much less likely to impair competition. This assumption, however, seems oversimplified. Economic theory suggests two ways in which freedom of entry may arguably be pertinent. First, the advent of new companies may serve to erode the immediate gains in relative size that accompany a merger. This result, however, is certainly not inevitable.... The other use for such evidence would be to demonstrate that potential competition will necessarily be such a threat that it will prevent a dominant firm from exercising its market power in a harmful way....

He reached a two-fold conclusion:

(1) ... potential firms are no substitute for actual companies in preserving such noneconomic advantages as the independence of small business, local initiative, and maximum career opportunity.

(2) ... low entry barriers may not keep a dominant firm from raising prices. Such a firm may feel that the profits to be gained before the

---

[12] Brief on Behalf of Defendants, p. 111.

[13] H. F. Houghton, The Anatomy of a Merger, Antitrust Bulletin, March-April 1961, Vol. 6, No. 2.

[14] D. C. Bok, Section 7 of the Clayton Act and the Merging of Law and Economics, Harvard Law Review, Vol. 74, No. 2, December 1960, pp. 226, 260-61.

arrival of new entrants will be large enough to outweigh the advantages
of charging a price so low as to discourage entry.

Entry in Merger Litigation

To sum up, consideration of entry in merger litigation[15] is
redundant, when a showing is made of structural alteration in
the form of a significant increase in concentration. New entrants
normally are small marginal firms entering and leaving. Such
entrants have no real effect on market structure or market conditions. Basically, the question is whether any new entrants can
manage to upgrade to the point of having any impact on the top
layer of concentrated control, where price and output matters
are determined. In oligopolistic industries, barriers to entry
are formidable. Hence the entry condition will usually reinforce,
rather than dilute, the legislative tests, which are the showing of
the probable lessening of competition or tendency to monopoly.

Entry in merger litigation has little in common with Bain's[16]
work. As Mr. Clodius points out, Bain defines entry as new firm
intervention resulting in an increase in industry capacity. It is
not to be expected that participants in antitrust controversy will
limit themselves to such a narrow definition. Indeed, entry is
commonly considered as potential competition from any source,
including expansionist activities of firms already in the business,
as well as that from substitute products. Bain also emphasizes
potential entry as a restraint on market control. While this may
be relevant to a Sherman Act case, it could hardly be applied to
merger cases concerned with incipient monopoly. Moreover, it
is a factor extremely difficult, if not impossible, to assess empirically. Finally, he examines the question of the extent to which
barriers to entry might be reduced in order to make competition
more workable or to achieve better performance. This goes beyond the field of existing antitrust laws into the area of new legislation — and the analysis is not oriented in that direction. Thus,
the tool users could not readily develop or implement a program
on the basis of his study.

If the bridge of communication between tool makers and tool

---

[15]Other cases in which a showing of lack of entry has influenced the courts or the
Federal Trade Commission to rule against mergers include Crown, Spalding, Scott,
Pillsbury and Union Carbide. In two cases, on the other hand, Jerrold Electronics
and Columbia Pictures, great opportunity for new companies to enter the relevant
markets influenced the courts to approve mergers. See Betty Bock, Mergers and
Markets, National Industrial Conference Board, 1962, pp. 112-16 and 45.

[16]J. S. Bain, Barriers to New Competition, Harvard University Press, Cambridge, 1956.

users breaks down, traditional "horse-sense" will take over, and
a sort of Gresham's law will evolve where those concerned with
the pursuit of victory will drive out of circulation those in pursuit of truth.

WILLARD F. WILLIAMS
Oklahoma State University │ *DISCUSSION*

PROFESSOR CLODIUS has exhibited ability and craftsman-
ship in developing an interesting and stimulating chapter. I
agreed with much of what he had to say. I, nevertheless,
found the task of evaluating his remarks to be a difficult assignment. The subject matter suggested by the title is complex, representing a frontier area in which there are few established guidelines. As indicated by the opening paragraph, the chapter goes even
beyond this broad assignment. It exposes some of the more involved and controversial aspects of market structure theory for
reconsideration. I found myself concerned and disturbed on several counts and offering qualifications in different, even opposite,
directions simultaneously. Much of the discussion is cast in
terms of theory according to Bain, to which I take marked exception on numerous points.

In much of the remaining portion of the discussion, theory
seems to have been relegated to a role of objectionably minor
importance. I share his concern regarding weaknesses and dangers inherent in the conventional or "pure theory" approach to
formulation of policy and public programs. I hope to add a mul-
tiplier effect to this concern. I am not at all certain that entirely
satisfactory operational criteria connecting performance norms
and public programs can or should be developed by economics
alone or in combination with other disciplines. But I am not prepared to say that theory cannot make a significant contribution to
this problem. Nor am I persuaded that significant improvements
in theory must await findings of many empirical studies.[1]

Clodius makes a good case for his assertion that "... we do
not know reliable and predictable relationships between condition
of entry and market performance" and that these are essential to
formulation of operational criteria. But he makes an equally good
case for concluding that there are so many unsolved theoretical

[1]By "improvements in theory" I simply mean conceptualization toward a more
completely systematized and consistent body of thought than presently is available
for use in market structure analysis.

questions and difficult problems of measurement that establishment of predictable relationships is virtually impossible. Having
destroyed his own best arguments for market structure research,
he is forced, it seems to me, to operational criteria which require
neither theory nor research. I find the suggested alternative,
Clodius' "second" or "pragmatic" approach, equally as weak and
fully as dangerous as the one which I believe he mislabels as "the
pure theory approach." While neither theory nor research may
ever provide fully satisfactory guides to policy formulation, I
find myself more confident than Clodius seems to be that both
can eventually provide policy makers with useful tools.

These remarks deserve some amplification. I am constrained
by the nature of the chapter and my own inclinations to spend what
might be considered an inordinate amount of time on basic questions of a theoretical nature.

CURRENT THEORY RELATING TO MARKET
PERFORMANCE AND SOCIAL WELFARE

Current market structure theory focuses attention first and
primarily upon the institutional characteristics of markets rather
than upon performance. In a capitalist economy in which the current theory has been fashioned primarily by analytical institu-
tionalists, this is not surprising. It is interesting and seemingly
rather inconsistent, however, since theorists and empiricists
alike admit that the focal aim of market structure analysis presumably is to arrive at implications and recommendations for
public policy designed, in turn, to enhance social welfare. Although performance might be considered the heart of current
market structure theory, it also is the Achilles heel.

Bain and others apparently have had no intention of developing
a truly general theory of market performance. Instead, they
have been interested in theory that would permit and guide research dealing with hypothesized relationships among roughly
defined aspects and dimensions of structure, conduct and performance. Bain, among others, clearly suggests that structure
and conduct do not fully determine performance; he claims only
that these factors probably do systematically affect performance.[2]

---

[2]Bain states that "Market structure and conduct clearly represent only a small
fraction of the total determinants of market performance...." He indicates that
when we make the statement that structure and conduct determine performance
"...the most we can mean is that given the character of all other important and
perhaps more basic determinants, they 'make a difference' in how performance will
emerge...." J. S. Bain, Industrial Performances, John Wiley & Sons, Inc., New
York, 1959.

Thus, in rather completely adopting the orientation and approach
of the institutionalist, the theory is immediately cast in a rather
rigid framework in which there are strong tendencies to neglect
or ignore many relevant considerations. Included among these,
it appears, are (1) factors which in some instances might affect
performance fully as much or more than those defined as structural variables and (2) detailed consideration of market performance within the larger framework of relationships between multidimensional aspects of performance and social welfare. I am
most concerned at this point with the fact that the conceptual
ground beyond specification of interrelationships is swampy and
uncharted.[3] A result is that there are many obvious weaknesses
and dangers in the accepted orientation or approach as it relates
to specification of operational criteria and to development of public policy programs.

Considerable lip service is given in the literature to welfare
implications of market performance.[4] But apparently accepted
definitions of performance, while pragmatic in a static, determin-
istic sense, tend to impound demand considerations, to freeze effects of shifts and variations in demand or supply and de-emphasize
the role of price and the consumer.[5] Furthermore, in establishing
particular aspects or dimensions of "ideal" or "workable" competition or performance, Bain and others depart rather sharply from
types of welfare-oriented dimensions one might expect to follow
from their definitions and extended discussions. Dimensions of
performance are cast largely in terms of operational efficiency.[6]

---

[3] Among questions raised are those concerning (1) the welfare aims and goals of
society, (2) definitions, dimensions, types and degrees of performance, (3) economic
criteria for determining acceptability or relevance of specific dimensions or degrees of performance, (4) types, kinds and degrees of performance that might be
considered "ideal" from the standpoint of focal welfare aims, (5) performance norms
for determining conditions in which it is "consistent with," "opposed to," or "independent of" social welfare goals or interests or in some sense "satisfactory or acceptable," "unsatisfactory or unacceptable," or "workable or unworkable," (6) objective and subjective measures of performance, (7) implications of performance
with respect to public policy and (8) structure, conduct and performance implications of specified policy remedies.
[4] Bain, for instance, describes a concept referred to as "ideal performance"
which he defines in terms of broad economic objectives relating to employment,
efficiency, income distribution, etc. Bain, op. cit., p. 15.
[5] In elaborating on his definition of market performance, Bain says, for example,
that it "... refers to the character of end adjustments to effective demands for their
outputs which are made by sellers (or adjustments made by buyers to effective supplies of outputs)." Bain, op. cit., p. 11.
[6] Profits or the height of price relative to cost of production is one of Bain's few
performance dimensions other than physical efficiency that might be considered some
measure of welfare implications. But like most of Bain's "dimensions" it is a measure rather than an economic or welfare criterion. In addition, Bain himself seems
to admit that it is a rather crude yardstick subject to many limitations. Although he

Other economic criteria related closely to welfare aims and those
provided by concepts which agricultural economists have loosely
included under the term "pricing efficiency" are largely neglected.[7] Little reference is made to such things as (1) the need
to balance social gains associated with greater product variety
with the extra cost and inconvenience of buying and selling in
markets of many differentiated products, (2) effects upon structure and performance of differences and variations in knowledge
of various types and (3) relevance or role of nonregulatory or
service types of public- or industry-sponsored programs such as
marketing information, uniform grading and quality standardization.

The difficulty in finding or developing either objective or subjective measures of pricing efficiency probably is one of the reasons why measures of operational efficiency are made to play
such a prominent role. The pragmatic, institutional and research-
oriented nature of the theory, however, contributes to this difficulty. I am not at all convinced that any conceptual framework
should be bounded or affected by availability of conveniently
measured dimensions. This, certainly, was not true in development of classical or even modern theory. It sounds reasonable
and logical to say that theory and research should develop hand
in hand, but this is not the way that significant contributions to
theory have developed in the past.

Alternatives to the "Pure Theory" Approach

Clodius suggests that there are only two sets of criteria for
judging public programs affecting market structures. The one,
he says, appears unsatisfactory because it involves arbitary performance goals, established operational criteria in relation to
goals, and leads to consideration of individual structural variables
and to policies designed to optimize with respect to each such
variable. That there are many dangers and weaknesses inherent

---

mentions character of product including design, quality and variety, these dimensions
are not clearly and pointedly related and oriented to the character of demand or the
nature and variety of consumer preference. Casual reference to "buyer's desires"
generally assume uniform preference functions.

[7]Conspicuously absent from many lists of performance dimensions are those
associated with (1) efficiency of the marketing system in developing and organizing
information on factors affecting demand, supply, prices and values, (2) efficiency in
transmitting this information from one point in the marketing system to another,
forward to consumers, and backward to raw material producers and the factor markets and (3) efficiency and effectiveness of processing, manufacturing and service
agencies in translating available information and consumer desires, values and
preferences into quantity, quality, design and variety of product produced.

in such an approach is unquestioned. The current state of market structure theory as it relates to performance, social welfare and remedial programs raises a wide variety of complex questions and plunges the investigator into a tangled web of conflicting views and persuasions. I suggest, however, that there are many theoretical or philosophical approaches — perhaps as many as there are market structure analysts. I see no particular reason why this one necessarily should involve consideration of individual structural variables. Accordingly, the label "pure theory approach" seems inappropriate; the procedure described simply is one rather naïve approach. I contend, as I have already, that any more sophisticated and useful approach will require additional extension, development and refinement of theory.

The disappointing aspect of Clodius' chapter is that it does not carry us very far toward a more meaningful or useful alternative.[8] His second or "completely pragmatic" view involves specification of "geniune problems" such as those associated with economic power or growth, and the search on a trial-and-error basis for appropriate remedies. Historical experience — success of the program in implementing the policy and solving the problem — is the recommended criterion. He would take a look at an industry such as steel, formulate the problem as one of economic power, decide on some basis that size was the principal contributing factor of a malleable nature — far outweighing other considerations — and adopt appropriate policies and programs. Empirical studies providing information on relationships between aspects of structure and performance apparently would be utilized.

This approach surely does have the appeal of pragmatism. It is pure institutionalism and seems to completely deny the relevance of theory in connecting dimensions of performance and social welfare goals and requires relatively little empirical investigation. Although it may have some usefulness in fairly obvious examples such as that provided by the steel industry, it reduces the entire field of market structure analysis in less clearly defined or marginal situations to nothing more than Bain's "horseback judgment."[9] Both Bain and Clodius, it seems to me, place entirely too much emphasis and reliance upon human judgment. To the extent possible this is the direction we want to move from, not toward.

Alternative approaches, I believe, either are available or can be developed. Some combination of the two approaches, for

---

[8] In describing the "completely pragmatic" view he seems to adopt Bain's philosophy that "...the long-term tendency in performance of an industry is a sufficient criterion of its fulfilling the material welfare goals." Bain, op. cit., p. 340.

[9] Bain, op. cit., p. 12.

instance, seems infinitely superior to either of the two considered separately. I think theory can do a better job than has been done thus far of specifying or providing (1) relevant dimensions of performance, (2) hypotheses regarding economic aspects of differences or variations in performance, (3) guides to <u>directions</u> of particular dimensions or combinations of dimensions that can be considered "desirable" or "acceptable" and (4) conceptual bases for determining economic consequences of private or public programs designed to change or alter performance.

THE CONCEPTS OF STRUCTURE AND CONDUCT
AS RELATED TO ENTRY AND EXIT

There appear to be at least two major weaknesses in the currently accepted conceptual framework as it relates specifically to structure and conduct. The first, mentioned earlier, is that it does not give adequate recognition to factors other than structure which affect conduct and performance. Secondly, the definitions of structure and conduct are not as strictly observed as they might be in developing detailed specifications of characteristics, economic criteria and dimensions.

While several questions could be raised concerning the concept and definition of market structure, the accepted definition does seem to restrict structure rather specifically to characteristics of organization. A major difficulty seems to enter at this point. If the definition is strictly observed, it becomes necessary to introduce nonstructural determinants which tend to deemphasize the influence and role of structure. If, on the other hand, determinants other than organizational characteristics are included as structural dimensions, restrictions imposed by the definition are violated or stretched virtually beyond recognition. Bain, nevertheless, adopts the latter alternative.

"Strategic aspects" of market structure, according to Bain,[10] include degree of concentration, degree of product differentiation and the condition of entry. These, it seems to me, are <u>measures</u> of something or other and not, strictly speaking, organizational <u>characteristics</u>. Not all, except by a considerable stretch of the imagination, are <u>measures</u> of such characteristics. Number and size distributions of buyers and sellers, variations among firms with respect to degree of specialization or diversification and other aspects of type or class, degree of vertical or horizontal integration and location of geographic distribution all, it seems

---

[10] Bain, <u>op. cit.</u>, p. 12.

to me, are primarily structural characteristics. Some of these, although sometimes included by implication, frequently are not pointedly and expressly mentioned as organizational character- istics. On the other hand, degree of product differentiation and conditions of entry nearly always are classed as structural di- mensions. That they are related in some fashion to market structure is clear. The dominant form of relationship, however, seems to be in the nature of the effects of organizational charac- teristics flowing through market conduct rather than integral parts of the organizational complex.

Entry and Exit: Concepts and Measurement

Condition of entry presents a more difficult problem. Such conditions undoubtedly are related closely to structure and affect conduct, but entry conditions also are affected by conduct and by factors which also give rise to organizational changes. From the standpoint of any one given industry, entry is not strictly an or- ganizational characteristic and certainly cannot be classified as strategy or behavior. In a theoretically closed economy of one industry it is irrelevant. In a multi-industry economy it is a measure of competitive relations between the industry in question and potential entrants and for this reason might be an indicator of intra-industry structural relations. From the standpoint of a particular industry, however, entry is a nonstructural condition or situation arising out of technical economic relationships and of conduct which may lead to or tend to be associated with certain structural forms.[11] Accordingly, I would be inclined to set these conditions apart under some aspect of competition such as "intra- industry competition" and consider them to be closely interrelated with both industry structure and conduct.

Clodius seems to imply, and I agree, that in some respects Bain's treatment of entry, characteristically, is excessively sim- plified. Bain explains clearly how and why entry might be pre- cluded as barriers rise. His theoretical framework, however, does not formally explain (1) why a particular barrier level may preclude entry in one industry or at one period of time and prove ineffectual in another industry or at another time, or (2) why

---

[11] Economies of scale, it seems to me, either are or are not an economic fact of life which may have developed independently of structure and which may lead simul- taneously to a particular structure and barriers to entry. Absolute cost advantages and price or cost advantages of product differentiation, listed by Bain as additional factors affecting condition of entry, also are economic conditions. They are condi- tions arising out of conduct which are designed to change or alter structure.

entry may be as effectively precluded at the zero barrier level as at some particular high level.

This suggests the desirability of additional thought and effort directed toward improvements in the theory. I should think that the idea of "incentives to entry" might help. As barriers rise, according to Bain, an increase takes place in the extent to which established sellers can persistently elevate their prices above the competitive level.[12] But as prices rise incentives to entry also rise. This idea could be expressed in a simple diagram with cost of entry and some measure of incentives to entry expressed on vertical scales. Product prices, with the competitive level of price near the origin, would be indicated on the horizontal scale. Effectiveness of the barriers would be determined by the levels and shapes of the two functions.

This approach and similar alternatives present some obvious problems. The point is, however, that Bain is not necessarily the last word on matters of theory. Many opportunities for additional contributions clearly are available.

Clodius urges us to initiate studies to establish relationships between conditions of entry and market performance. In the absence of such relationships, he says, "... it is idle and misleading to formulate either operational criteria or public programs concerning entry and exit." But he is greatly impressed with obstacles in the form of theoretical inconsistencies and problems of measurement to establishment of such relationships. His conclusion, it seems to me, is that, therefore, we must adopt a pragmatic approach in which neither theory nor measurement is needed. In my view this conclusion is not fully justified by his arguments. Others appear admissible.

I agree, nevertheless, with most of what Clodius has to say regarding problems and difficulties involved in measuring barriers. Bain's price measure seems less than entirely adequate. He recognizes the importance of nonprice forms of competition in imperfectly competitive situations and admits that for one reason or another firms in such situations frequently do not fully exploit their price-raising potentials. How, then, is the extent to which firms <u>can</u> persistently raise prices to be measured? A related question arises as to the measurement of the competitive level of prices. Hypothetical competitive price levels will differ or vary according to assumptions made. Are they reflected by costs of existing firms or by hypothetical costs of firms in hypothetically competitive market structures? But surely all is not lost. Until better evidence becomes available let us at least hope

---

[12]Bain, <u>op. cit.</u>, p. 237.

optimistically that improved devices for measuring barriers to
entry and relationships between entry and performance will be
developed. This is a fertile field for the constructive suggestions
that are missing from the chapter by Professor Clodius.

The treatment by Professor Clodius of the exit problem is,
perhaps, the major contribution of the chapter. I agree emphatically with the idea that exit involves something different from
negative parallelism with respect to entry. Additional work on
the exit problem of a conceptual nature as well as continued empirical investigation, however, is needed.

Several minor points might be raised. For instance, I see
little reason why his asset demand function necessarily would
rise with improvements in the liquidity status of the potentially
egressing firm. The acquiring firm always can trade liquid assets
for other liquid assets without bothering with those of economically distressed firms. Secondly, his statement that "in normative models the ultimate public good is served or denied as firms
either do or do not enter and leave" seems to go a bit too far.
Third, I fail to see the logic behind the suggestion that we attempt
to synthesize an optimum entrant.

Finally, logic and the present state of the arts in market structure analysis suggest caution in arriving at conclusions regarding
the market power of industry executives. This includes the President as well as Professor Clodius. That the nation's 500 largest
industrials made 57 per cent of the sales and 72 per cent of the
profits of all such firms undoubtedly is fact. By themselves, however, such facts are not sufficient to conclude (1) that executives
of the 500 are in position to show "utter contempt" for the public
and (2) that, therefore, any or all public policy remedies are justified or in the public interest simply because they are effective.

Chapter 6

STEPHEN H. SOSNICK

University of California

Operational criteria for evaluating market performance

SYNOPSIS

THIS CHAPTER has three broad subdivisions. The first deals with the concept of market performance. In this section I review the prevailing interpretation and make some comments concerning the internal consistency of current usage.

In the second section I review the generally recognized dimensions of market performance and undertake to appraise the adequacy of their classification.

The third section pertains to specifying dimension norms for performance. Here I comment on prevailing norms and propose some alternatives. The norms considered relate to 12 performance dimensions: production efficiency, technological progressiveness, product suitability, profit rates, level of output, exchange efficiency, cost of sales promotion, unethical practices, participant rationality, conservation, external effects and labor relations.

I.   THE CONCEPT OF MARKET PERFORMANCE

Prevailing Usage

Not very long ago the social performance of industries and firms was measured by their "1. Employment...2. Production ...3. Consumer Effort Commanded...4. Consumer Funds Absorbed...5. Payrolls...6. Dividends and Interest."[1]

Current reaction to this approach is unfavorable. Thus Bain comments:

---

[1] T. J. Kreps and K. R. Wright, Measurement of the Social Performance of Business, United States Temporary National Economic Committee Monograph No. 7, Washington, 1940, pp. 3-4.

In general, it is not appropriate to measure the market performance of an enterprise or industry in such terms as its contribution...to total employment in the economy, the total output of goods, or the stability over time of either. This is because (in the case of sellers, for example) the essential limits of the performance of enterprises within a capitalist economy are those of adjusting to whatever effective demands are present for their outputs, with the restriction that in so adjusting they must as a group at least "break even"....[2]

The current approach is that firms will and should respond to their individual opportunities and restraints. According to Clodius and Mueller, "Market performance refers to the economic results that flow from the industry as an aggregate of firms."[3] Similarly, according to Bain, the term refers "to the strategic end results of market adjustments engaged in by sellers and buyers" (p. 340). The adjustments involved are "adjustments to the effective demands for their outputs which are made by sellers (or adjustments made by buyers to the effective supplies of outputs).... The character of end adjustments...[is to be considered] relative perhaps to some...ideal.... The principal aspects or dimensions of market performance include prominently: profits, scale and utilization of plants and firms, sales promotion costs, character of the product and progressiveness" (pp. 11-12).[4]

The essential word here is "results." While many of us have often used the word, it now strikes me as needing more clarification than has been given.

Needed Clarifications

In the first place, one probably should not take literally the statement that performance consists of results of adjustments to effective demand or supply. Innovation and advertising are to be included, and they can be said to create or shift demand or supply, as well as to respond to it.

In the second place, no one really intends to include in the performance category every market attribute that is a result of market adjustments. To do so would destroy the distinction between the performance of a market and its structure and conduct.

---

[2] J. S. Bain, Industrial Organization, John Wiley & Sons, Inc., New York, 1959, p. 11. Further references to this volume will be by page citation only.

[3] R. L. Clodius and W. F. Mueller, "Market Structure Analysis as an Orientation for Research in Agricultural Economics," Journal of Farm Economics, August 1961, pp. 515-33.

[4] Clodius and Mueller, op. cit., p. 517, observe "The framework and concepts [Bain] sets forth appear to represent the current general consensus of scholars in the general area...." One might even say "establish the general consensus."

Structure and conduct would be included in the category of performance because they too are results. Thus, seller concentration, buyer concentration, the degree of product differentiation, the condition of entry and vertical integration, along with firms' policies concerning prices, products, sales promotion, collusion and predation are all results in the sense that they are influenced by other market attributes or conditions.[5]

Similarly, market demand and the legal form of business organizations, whether or not they are regarded as aspects of structure-conduct, are influenced by other market conditions, yet are nowhere regarded as part of performance.

Third, the exclusion of certain results from the performance category cannot be explained on the grounds that the excluded market attributes are intermediate results, while the included attributes are final results. Many excluded attributes are in fact influenced by the very results that are called "performance." Thus, "large" profits may induce vertical integration[6] or may

---

[5] Indeed, seller (and buyer) concentration of physical or dollar volume is a result in a sense that apparently is not commonly recognized. The ex post distribution of sales (and purchases) cannot be an attribute of market structure. It is part of the trading outcome, which market structure supposedly influences.

What each seller — and market analysis — starts with is a set of reservation prices. (In a situation where output is variable, the reservation prices represent the marginal cost function or, more simply, a production capacity.) The proportion that each seller has of all intramarginal reservation prices, or of total capacity, constitutes ex ante concentration. The ex post distribution of sales in a period is, as duopoly theory recognizes, the result of this ex ante distribution plus market conduct.

How the two distributions compare in practice is something that remains to be explored. The exploration is not encouraged by viewing the ex post distribution as an explanatory variable instead of one to be explained, or by referring to scale economies as a determinant of the concentration of sales instead of the concentration of capacity.

One can reply, to be sure, that ex post concentration "explains" profit rates, in the sense that the two are correlated, and that it would be foolish either to neglect this relation or to substitute in as the independent variable something as speculative as ex ante concentration, at least until its effects are more clearly understood.

For the present, this reply is satisfactory, provided we realize that ex post concentration may be a proxy variable. That is, the correlation between it and profits may arise because both are correlated with — this time, result from — ex ante concentration. And provided also that we sharpen our definitions. As M. Shubik observes, "Economic usage has often failed to distinguish between the objective background of a market and the behavior of the participants which determines the market outcome." (Strategy and Market Structure, New York, 1959, p. 11.)

The objective background may be subdivided. One part is market structure, consisting of the relevant environmental constraints or opportunities to which participants must adapt, at least for the time being. The other part, which includes the ex ante distribution, is participant characteristics, consisting of the relevant properties of participants' states of mind and material.

[6] See the analysis in W. F. Mueller and L. Garoian, Changes in the Market Structure of Grocery Retailing, University of Wisconsin Press, Madison, 1961, Chapter 5.

attract competitive entry that modifies concentration and pricing policies.[7]

There is, in other words, no uni-directional causal sequence that runs from nonresults to results, and no set of attributes that can be identified as performance because they occupy final position in a causal sequence. Virtually every market attribute is influenced by other market attributes, and the chain of influence is circular and endless. To speak of end results, then, will be misleading if we interpret "end" to mean final.

Fourth, what does explain the exclusion of certain results or attributes from the performance category is that not all results are equally interesting. Economists are seldom intrigued by the fact that water flows from the roof-ends of buildings as a result of locating plants in rainy regions in response to local effective demand. What is interesting, of course, depends on the observer's purposes.

The principal purpose of economists in this context stems from their traditional concern with the amount and distribution of real social income. Certain market attributes appear to be, as Bain puts it (p. 340), "the crucial indicator and measure of how well the market activity of enterprises contributes to the enhancement of material welfare." That is, certain results are especially interesting because they appear to influence the attainment of putative private and social goals directly, whereas other results exert their influence on private and social welfare indirectly, via their impact on the strategic results. The latter then become the subject of ends-in-view for a socially oriented observer, and are categorized and emphasized by being called "performance."

Fifth, the interesting attributes should be evaluated as a response to whatever opportunities and constraints happen to be presented by the individual market situation; the basis, however, can be pragmatic as well as ideological.

The pragmatic basis is that it is feasible and convenient to proceed to appraise and correct certain welfare losses associated with individual markets (such as excessive advertising) as if certain other issues (such as legality of sale of the product, correctness of input prices and aggregate unemployment) were resolved by other means. The pragmatic basis seems to me sound for a market economy, whether it is capitalistic, socialistic, etc.

---

[7] Similarly, excess capacity may lead to horizontal mergers and price discrimination. "Large" sales promotion costs may enhance product differentiation and conduce to vertical mergers. Substantial durability and frequent model changes may alter market demand and increase the obstacles to entry. Rapid progressiveness may contribute to rapid turnover of competitors and encourage diversification, reciprocal dealing, patent sharing and use of corporate subsidiaries.

The ideological basis is that it is inconsistent with capitalism to expect adjustments that imply financial losses. I do not find this basis comfortable.

One reason is that alterations in public policy (and in prices, such as land rent) can convert unprofitable adjustments into profitable ones, and vice versa. Subsidies or prohibitions, for example, can create or destroy an effective demand. As a result, a no-loss restraint is meaningful only after a rather complete specification of public policy.

Another reason is that one of the purposes of study here is in fact to suggest where and how public policy should make these conversions. This purpose is not accomplished if unsatisfactory results are condoned because they are dictated by profitability.

Appraisals pertaining to a capitalistic economy must make some debatable concessions to incentives and characteristics that are inherent in capitalism (relating, for example, to acquisitiveness and property income), and rather compelling reasons should be given if the implication is to introduce additional subsidies, controls, state competition, etc. To do more, however, could transform appraisal into apologetics.[8]

In short, what is really intended by the term "market performance" — or what apparently will be meant if contradictions are avoided — is the attributes of production and exchange in a segment of the economy that directly influence the welfare of the participants and the society. These attributes represent some, but not all, of the results of participants' adjustments to expected demand and supply opportunities in the market, and of adjustments to other things too. The attributes include the results that directly affect people's well-being, whatever results these may be in particular kinds of markets and regardless of whether they in turn act on the conditions that affected them. And they may be recognized and deplored even if they happen to result from, or be required for, avoiding losses.

II.   THE DIMENSIONS OF MARKET PERFORMANCE

According to Bain:

The particular set of performance dimensions which are analytically significant varies from industry to industry.... A certain few broad aspects

---

[8] The question of ideological bias would seem relevant, for example, if the fact that price does not equal marginal cost passes unmentioned simply because it would (without a subsidy) imply financial losses, or if no reference is made to undeveloped flood control, navigation, recreation, conservation and archeology simply because they would not be remunerative.

of performance, to be sure, are important in all industries, for instance, the efficiency of the industry in terms of the [p. 356: horizontal and vertical] scales of plants and firms, the relation of price to [p. 12: average] cost as reflected in the profit rate, and the size of selling costs in relation to sales revenue. But in each of numerous groups of industries some additional or "special" aspect of performance . . . will be of great importance (pp. 340-41).

Four such added dimensions of performance are: technological progressiveness, product performance, conservation performance, and price flexibility (p. 394). [Furthermore, in] the steel industry, we would find that with disparately located production centers and a product with high weight and shipping cost relative to its value, the relationship of delivered prices (inclusive of delivery freight) among various buyer locations is a dimension of performance of substantial importance, whereas for the great majority of goods and industries the geographical pricing pattern is a minor matter (p. 341).

Adequacy of Identification

One question to raise is whether the mentioned attributes of production and exchange in a market are in fact directly significant. I do not doubt it.

Another question is whether the mentioned attributes represent the issues that are generally important. Here I do have some doubts. It appears that some important issues closely related to those mentioned have been omitted, and that some others have been omitted that one might not consider from examining the list given.

Production Efficiency. Production efficiency comprehends much more than scale, utilization and vertical integration. It includes also locating plants at cost-minimizing sites; attainment of the highest production function; minimization of featherbedding, sinecures, lobbying and extravagances; appropriate input proportions; control of input and output inventories; procurement at the best places, sources, times and quantities; regularity of operations; utilization of by-products; appropriate diversification and decentralization; minimum billing and collection costs; and minimum distractions by purely financial matters. Perhaps it makes sense to bypass these issues on the grounds that they are a separate subject — namely, firms' "internal efficiency."

But production efficiency relates also to equalization of marginal costs among plants; to avoidance of wasteful duplications; to achievement of synchronization and coordination (as contrasted, for example, with competitive exploitation of an oil field); to imposition of minimum trouble on suppliers (e.g., peak loads) and customers (e.g., separate terminals); to minimum costs of

adaptation to uncertainties; and to minimum turnover among firms
and other losses from discontinuity.

I can see no reason to bypass these issues. They too are in-
extricably related to market organization. And an applicable
minimum optimal scale is not determinate except simultaneously
with adjustments also in these directions.

Technological progressiveness is, of course, closely related.
We might emphasize the relation by treating progressiveness as
a phase of production efficiency, just as product improvement has
been treated as a phase of product suitability. However, enough
issues of a different kind may be involved to make a separate
heading convenient. It does not really matter whether we call the
persistence of antiquated high-cost techniques (such as soil levees
in rice production) "inefficient" or "unprogressive," so long as
we understand that the issue is relevant.

Price-Cost Relations. The relation of price to average cost
is a questionable indicator of the results that evidently are really
at issue. According to Bain, a persistent divergence between
price and average cost has two kinds of significance. One is its
implication for profit rates and therefore its impact on "maintaining efficient production under an enterprise system" (p. 369)
and on "inequality of income distribution" (p. 371). The other is
its implication for restriction of output via differences among
industries in "the relationship of price to average cost — and also,
in general, to long-run marginal cost," and therefore its impact
on "the allocation of resources among uses" (p. 371).

Neither the level nor the inter-industry rank of profit rates,
however, seems to me to be implied by the level or rank of the
excess of price over average cost. Before a profit rate can be
inferred from a given excess, it needs to be, first, multiplied by
quantity and, second, divided by the investment assignable to
whichever product is being considered. Even in the usual text-
book situation (where each quantity is associated with a single,
known excess, investment and profit) there are two rates of profit
associated with each excess (except where it equals zero or the
most profitable gap) and up to four excesses associated with each
rate of profit. As a result, it would seem simpler to consider
what is really at issue — profit rates — directly.

Similarly, neither the level nor the inter-industry rank nor
even the existence of output restriction seems to me to be implied
by the level or rank or existence of the excess. Before an amount
of restriction can be inferred, account must be taken of the non-
identity of quantity produced and quantity sold, or the elasticity
of buyers' demand, of the short-run marginal social cost of increasing output and of the price-marginal cost relation in competing industries.

Not even the limiting case (which includes the first intersection of demand with a u-shaped average cost and the equilibrium position with monopolistic competition) is clear to me — that industries with "no excess profits are not restricting their outputs below a competitive level" (p. 372). A fortiori, it would also seem to be simpler for other cases to refer directly to what is really at issue — the level of output. To do so may also be more revealing, since it seems to be possible for the level of output to be objectionable even if there is no unjustifiable excess of price over average cost.

Exchange Efficiency. The level of output is not the only issue raised by asking about the impact of a market on the allocation of resources among uses. Also important is how well the quantity available (whether carryover or current production) leaves the hands of persons who value the commodity least and ends up in the hands of persons who value it most. This issue is, for example, at the heart of the argument for replacing agricultural price supports by direct payments, and is intimately involved in an appraisal of "orderly marketing."

Indeed, for certain markets efficiency of exchange is the principal issue involved. These markets are the ones that used to come to mind when the word "market" was used — bazaars, exchanges, auctions, sealed bidding sites, agents' and dealers' activities — in general, environments in which items are sold.

For such markets what influences people's welfare is "the outcome" — that is, the contracts that are made and the economic implications of the contracts: quantity sold (perhaps expressed relative to the quantity indicated by the demand-supply intersection), average price (perhaps relative to the intersection price), price dispersion and convergence, distribution among buyers and sellers of the gains from trade, the success in trading of intramarginal versus extramarginal participants and the amount of transfer costs incurred (transportation, commissions, taxes, yardage, recordation, etc.). These are the dimensions of market performance that are emphasized in short-run price theory.

The perspective has been broadened in the literature of industrial organization, as it has been in long-run price theory, to include attributes of production. But in the process, the exchange function of markets seems to have been forgotten. The explanation may lie in the fact that the exchange process is quasi-automatic in certain administered-price markets, so that all interesting attributes of the outcome can be summarized merely by the level of output, price or profit.[9] In general, however, to omit

---

[9] Thus, suppose that there is a nondiscriminating monopolist who produces to order (in contrast to producing for inventory or for immediate sale at a central

the subject of exchange efficiency will neglect something that is in all markets relevant and in some markets critical.

We can, furthermore, regard any actually identifiable ill effects of price flexibility as one aspect of exchange efficiency. To do so may provide a convenient way to approach the subject if, in the abstract, we do not know "what difference it makes if a price is more or less flexible in response to changes in demand and cost" (Bain, p. 403).

Sales Promotion. Sales promotion has a qualitative aspect as well as a quantitative one. The use of false or misleading advertising, labeling, packing, packaging, salesmen and market "news" is not unknown. Such practices seem to me significant even if "the size of selling costs in relation to sales revenue" is small. Similarly, even if sales promotion is not deceptive, it seems to me significant if information adequate for intelligent selection is not available.

We can summarize the significance of these qualitative aspects in an additional performance dimension. This is buyers' rationality — or, more generally, participants' rationality — in choosing among alternatives. Where exchange efficiency refers to the collective implementation of preferences, participant rationality refers to the individual formation of preferences.

Effects on participants' rationality (and on costs), however, may not adequately summarize the significance of deceitful sales promotion. In the minds of some people, duplicity is significant even if no material effects are identifiable. It is degrading, and it impairs the association of business survival with customer service. It therefore has a direct effect on welfare. With this attitude in mind, one might group together as an additional dimension of performance all forms of unethical practices.

Groupings, of course, are a matter of convenience, and the

---

market). Then all participants receive equal prices; there is no opportunity for price variation and convergence; there is no question as to whether extramarginal participants will succeed in buying and selling; and the level of average price, the level of quantity and the distribution of surplus among the participants are functionally related and capable of being summarized by one measure.

If, instead of a monopolist, there is a group of homogeneous oligopolists, the situation is different. Now the question of sellers' market shares appears. This question, however, can be couched in terms of the extent to which marginal costs are equalized among the oligopolists. It can thereby be regarded as one of the issues that will be recognized in connection with production efficiency. If so, then for this case too it would be unnecessary to recognize exchange efficiency as a separate issue.

Suppose, however, that the oligopolists' prices vary (because of different price policies, because of price discrimination, because of bargaining or because quantities are "thrown on the market"). Or suppose that cross-hauling or other locational problems are involved. Then the exchange process again has interesting alternatives that are not functionally related to the level of quantity or profits.

decision that certain attributes are performance is arbitrary. The important point is that unethical practices and participants' rationality are important issues that seem to have been neglected.[10]

Products. The issues involved here appear to be covered by the four aspects of product performance that Bain emphasizes: "(1) general level of quality or character of design of the products offered by the industry at any time; (2) rate and pattern of product change and improvement over time; (3) frequency of product change and improvement over time; and (4) variety among competing products at any time — all to be judged relative to alternatives, the comparative cost of the alternatives being taken into account" (p. 397).

Conservation. Exhaustible natural resources are especially interesting inputs because future price and quality may be importantly related to sellers' current practices. Other inputs, however, also may be managed favorably or unfavorably from a social viewpoint.

This variability seems to be particularly evident and assessable in the case of labor inputs. With labor, the principal issues apparently pertain to employee mobilization, to employee status, to employee attitudes and to collective bargaining.

External Effects. At least one other problem should be mentioned. The activities of sellers and/or buyers in a market may impose unreasonable burdens on outsiders or fail to provide them with appropriate benefits. The source of this problem is incomplete control and contract, and the relation may need clarification.

The law imposes a duty to refrain from injuring other persons in various ways. There are, thus, crimes, torts and zoning. For many other injuries, the law empowers persons to contract for avoidance. Thus a man may pay his neighbors to cease spraying or to modify a flow of water (but usually not, in the United States, to refrain from competing). As a result, injuries that are not prohibited outright or avoided voluntarily may be escaped by contract. If the disadvantaged can provide sufficient compensation, the injury may be prevented.

As to providing benefits, the law rarely imposes a duty to offer assistance or gifts to nonrelatives. The law does, however, empower persons to obtain many kinds of benefits (and to impose certain otherwise-prohibited losses) by contract. Thus, one may purchase various goods and services and licenses. As a result, various benefits that are not required by law or provided voluntarily may be acquired contractually. If the beneficiaries can

---

[10] The same might be said for "the diffusion of economic power" if it is something "valued for its own sake" (C. D. Edwards, Big Business and the Policy of Competition, Western Reserve University Press, Cleveland, 1956, pp. 2, 4).

provide sufficient compensation, the necessary steps may be taken.

In practice, however, people desiring to obtain benefits or to avoid injuries do not always have an adequate opportunity to provide sufficient compensation. The persons who must act in order to confer the benefit or avoid the injury, and also the persons who stand to gain, may be numerous and geographically dispersed; the effect on any one of the beneficiaries may be small and uncertain; the benefit may not be reasonably confinable to those who would contribute; and the cost of organization may be sizeable. As a result, it may not be feasible or worthwhile to make arrangements for compensation even though in principle it would be sufficient.

The principal significance of noncompensation is that it may imply a lack of inducement to confer the benefits or to avoid the burdens. People do provide many benefits and withhold innumerable burdens voluntarily, perhaps from altruism, habit and fear of informal punishment. Indeed, virtually every phase of living is modified because it affects others, and it would be unpleasant and inconvenient if everything had a price. But individuals are often helpless; people are not always sociable; and to confer benefits or avoid burdens sometimes involves more trouble and expense than even sociable people will assume.

Noncompensation may, as a result, lead to serious deficiencies. Unreasonable burdens may be imposed, such as warfare, nuisances, pollution, bee-killing residues, international difficulties, ugliness and destruction of relics. Or important but unremunerative benefits or services that the industry could most appropriately provide may go unprovided, such as flood control, recreation, pest eradication, knowledge and beauty. The welfare impact of a market includes such imposed burdens and unprovided benefits. They are not less its products because they happen to be unsaleable. [11]

The Task

In sum, evaluation of the attributes of a market that directly influence welfare involves consideration of at least the following twelve issues: (1) production efficiency, (2) technological progressiveness, (3) product suitability, (4) profit rates, (5) level of

[11] A few of the relevant references may be cited: W. J. Baumol, Welfare Economics and the Theory of the State, Harvard University Press, Cambridge, 1952. J. M. Clark, Social Control of Business, 2nd edition, McGraw Hill Book Co., New York, 1939. K. W. Kapp, Social Cost of Private Enterprise, Harvard University Press, Cambridge, 1950. A. C. Pigou, Economics of Welfare, 4th edition, The Macmillan Co., London, 1932.

output, (6) exchange efficiency, (7) cost of sales promotion, (8) unethical practices, (9) participant rationality, (10) conservation,
(11) external effects and (12) labor relations.

For each of these dimensions of performance we desire a
norm that will deplore results that are detectably less favorable
than unavoidable circumstances permit. The norm will be operational if it implies a set of feasible actions that will, for an actual
market situation, produce a dichotomous rating (such as "workable" or "unworkable") — or better, a quantification of actual versus optimum performance in the dimension at issue.

III.   DIMENSION NORMS FOR PERFORMANCE

Production Efficiency

There appears to be general agreement on a norm for production efficiency. The norm is that greater efficiency is desirable,
"measured by how closely firms in the industry approximate the
lowest attainable [real] costs for the outputs they produce and
distribute" (Bain, p. 342).

It appears, however, that it will be impossible for an observer
to decide how close to minimum costs an industry has come. Minimum costs are, in practice, not ascertainable.

Concerning "internal efficiency," there are too many problems
with managing labor (incentives, supervision, speed-up, etc.), too
many tasks being performed (run a time study or procurement
analysis on every one?), too many alternative ways of doing everything (consider every combination of possibilities?), too many
prior commitments (locations, assets, employees), too many imponderables (maintenance costs, accidents, etc.), too many ways to
adapt to variability and uncertainty (in demands, supplies, other
external conditions), too many ways to spread overhead (expand,
integrate, diversify), too many problems in allocating costs for
durable or joint inputs (lifetime, salvage value, depreciation
method, interest rate), too many ways in which supposedly comparable firms differ (input prices and qualities, output mixes,
etc.).

Concerning utilization of capacity, there are the problems of
expanding ahead of demand, of demand variability, of obsolete
capacity, and of whether it is cheaper to obtain a plant's minimum
average cost or to underutilize a larger plant.

Concerning economies of scale, there is the problem of time
for small firms to grow up, the problem of varying managerial
competence, the problem of multiple products, the problem of

increasing transportation costs, the problem of before-tax versus
after-tax optima and the problem of balancing variety versus
cost.[12] There is also an imponderable that derives from a fundamental asymmetry: With two or more firms, activities are decentralized; with one integrated firm, activities can be — but in
practice may not be — selectively centralized or decentralized as
is appropriate.

Only part of this asymmetry is recognized in the usual approach to economies of scale. It relates costs to a firm's absolute
output per year,[13] not to its proportion of total industry output.
As a result, it recognizes economies of absolute size, but not
economies of relative size.

At least four kinds of economies of relative size are always
potentially available: (1) elimination of needless duplication
(charter amendments, information-gathering, procurement, etc.),
(2) minimization of transport costs (local monopolies with appropriate spacing and unified assembly and/or delivery[14]), (3) coordination of interacting decisions (standardization, exchange of information) and (4) reduction of risk (competitive instability,
averaging out of local conditions, "economies of massed reserves,"[15] capital-market advantages).

Similarly, vertical integration in principle — but not necessarily in practice — always offers savings: (1) avoidance of costs
of exchange (advertising, search, agents, order-taking, haggling,

---

[12] Bain apparently does not regard variety as an important problem in appraising
efficiency, although he observes that "the size of the inefficient fringe ... (between
10 and 30 percent of industry output) ... did show some tendency to be larger in industries with strong product differentiation" (p. 353).

In contrast, E. H. Chamberlin asserts, "But unless it can be shown that the loss
of satisfaction from a more standardized product ... is less than the gain through
producing more units, there is no 'waste' at all, even though every firm is producing
to the left of its minimum point" ("Product Heterogeneity and Public Policy," American Economic Review, May 1950, p. 89). "What nonsense it is to compare the actual
price of a Rolls-Royce or of a Renault under monopolistic competition with the ruling price in a purely competitive Packard industry! Incidentally, the cost curves
would not even be those of the Packard Motor Company as presently constituted, because of the substantial external economies from standardization of parts and
methods on an industry-wide basis" (Monopoly and Competition and Their Regulation, The Macmillan Co., London, 1954, p. 259).

[13] In sophisticated versions, minimum attainable costs are shown to vary with
(1) output per hour or other lowest common denominator ("scale" referring to the
rate at which per-unit cost is minimum for a particular set of fixed inputs), and
(2) number of hours of production per year. See B. C. French, L. L. Sammet and
R. G. Bressler, "Economic Efficiency in Plant Operations with Special Reference to
the Marketing of California Pears," Hilgardia, July 1956, pp. 543-721.

[14] "Spatial monopoly creates an unstable situation and can be expected to result in
an excessive number of plants and correspondingly higher-than-optimum costs."
R. G. Bressler, "Pricing Raw Product in Complex Milk Markets," Agricultural Economics Research, October 1958, p. 119.

[15] E. A. G. Robinson, The Structure of Competitive Industry, The University of
Chicago Press, Chicago, 1958, p. 26.

billing, collecting, protections against dishonesty and default),
(2) coordination (exchange of information, synchronized expansion, harmonious scheduling, product selection[16]) and (3) marginal-cost pricing.

There is, of course, another side to the supposed economies of horizontal and vertical integration. It refers to inordinate complexity, to lack of incentives, to advantages of duplication and multiple centers of decision making, to maintenance of the "test of the market" and to the effectiveness of coordination "through the market."[17]

But the point is that when such imponderables must be considered, the level of minimum costs does not have an objective, replicable answer.

This is not at all to say that it is impossible to detect inefficiency. Certain departures from minimum costs may be quite apparent. Thus, featherbedding may be obvious. A sizeable proportion of a homogeneous product chronically may be produced in plants whose scale implies appreciably above-minimum production-plus-transportation costs. The utilization of the plants may be such that it would be cheaper to shut some down and concentrate production in the others. Inadequate vertical integration may be as noticeable as it now would be if steel, insurance and groceries were disintegrated.

The point is that an operational norm will not refer to minimum costs. It will specify merely that no real costs persist that are clearly unnecessary to provide the use-values that are being provided.

I would also add a qualification: No unnecessary real costs should persist without good reason. This qualification is not implicit if it is true that "Economists — notwithstanding all pretension to objectivity — have never doubted that laws are good if they promote efficiency and progress and bad if they thwart it."[18]

It is not a qualification that I can make definite. Its addition serves merely as a reminder of the potential conflict (arising because of uncompensated burdens) between efficiency and other values, and as an indication of willingness to sacrifice some efficiency in favor of sufficient advantages in other directions.

---

[16]See, for example, N. R. Collins, W. F. Mueller, and E. M. Birch, Grower-Processor Integration, California Agricultural Experiment Station Bulletin 768, 1959, esp. pp. 41-47.

[17]On the last see, for example, W. W. Cochrane, "Changing Structure of the American Economy: Its Implications for the Performance of Agricultural Markets," Journal of Farm Economics, May 1959, pp. 406-7. And F. A. Hayek, Individualism and Economic Order, The University of Chicago Press, Chicago, 1948, Chapter 4.

[18]D. J. Dewey, "Changing Standards of Economic Performance," American Economic Review, May 1960, p. 2.

What will constitute "sufficient advantages" I am not prepared to
state in the abstract, since it depends on the degree of affluence
already achieved and involves interpersonal comparisons of welfare and personal judgments as to desserts.[19]

Progressiveness

According to Bain, "the... appropriate... standard of evaluation... concerns how progressive the industry was relative to its
opportunities — how well it exploited the available opportunities
for invention and innovation.... An ideal rate of innovation through
time is one that promptly exploits every available technological
change which would reduce... cost... (the costs of innovation being taken into account) but that foregoes or delays technological
changes which, if made currently, would increase production
costs over time."

However, "we are unable to distinguish good from bad performance in the dimension.... Because there is no way of knowing, a priori, what unknown things can reasonably be expected to
be discovered... [the] 'potential' rate of discovery, against which
the actual rate might be measured, cannot in any way be systematically guessed.... [Similarly,] we would need to learn... not
only the long-run cost-reducing impact of each technological
change adopted (a relatively easy thing to learn), but also the
identities of all available opportunities for technological change
which were rejected, and the estimated effect on cost of each rejected opportunity."... "We cannot honestly do much more than
acknowledge the record of technological change... being grateful
for gifts received...." (pp. 395-97)

The obstacles to judging actual progressiveness relative
to the opportunities do appear to be insurmountable. I am
not convinced, however, that the observer is as helpless as might
be inferred. The problem seems to me analogous to that of appraising efficiency. Ideal performance is unknown (although here
it is also unknowable). Nevertheless, an observer will be able to
detect certain kinds of departures from ideal. An empirically applicable norm can specify that no such deficiencies persist without good reason. I have four kinds of deficiency in mind.

The first is misinvestment by the firms under consideration

---

[19]Among the potentially relevant advantages, however, one might mention long-
term progressiveness (perhaps from trade secrets), altered income distribution
(perhaps from inefficient work-sharing), worker satisfaction (perhaps from expensive working conditions), reduced insecurity (perhaps from costly seniority rules)
and smaller social dislocation (perhaps from slower economic development).

because they use an objectionable test of the worthwhileness of investment. The test applied may be objectionable because of the criterion that is used. The most felicitous criterion may be that additional investment should be accepted or rejected according to whether the ratio of the present value of its cash savings to the present value of its cash outlays, each being discounted at a socially appropriate rate, is greater than or less than unity. In contrast, firms may misinterpret the criterion (perhaps by miscalculating savings), or refer to a nonequivalent and objectionable criterion (such as adequate internal rate of return, three-year payback period, or replace-when-depreciated[20]) or undertake no systematic appraisal.

The test applied may also be objectionable because it employs a rate (or rates) of discount (or marginal cost of capital) that is too high or too low. The rate that is correct from a social viewpoint is arguable. But this does not mean that any rate that firms happen to use is unexceptionable. It is possible to show that a rate outside a particular range — perhaps three to 20 percent per year — is very likely to lead to overcapitalization or undercapitalization.[21] It is also possible to estimate what rate actually was used — by inference from the supplies of funds available to the firms, by reference to internal budgeting instructions, by analysis of projects undertaken or rejected and by inference from what rate would be used if management sought to maximize stockholders' wealth.[22]

A second kind of noticeable deficiency is suppression of inventions. Nonuse of an invention — even a patented one — is not in itself indicative of failure to make an appropriate innovation. The idea may be commercially premature or impractical. But nonuse does constitute suppression if it is coupled with a refusal to inform or license others that is either categorical or else conditional on fees or promises that would make their using it profitless. Suppression is an important problem in a country whose patent law does not require basic or reciprocal licensing.

---

[20] For discussion of such criteria, see, for example, J. Dean, "Measuring the Productivity of Capital," in E. Solomon, editor, Management of Corporate Capital, Free Press, Glencoe, 1959, pp. 21-34 (reprinted from the Harvard Business Review, 1954). According to Dean (p. 26), payback period "is unquestionably the most widely used measure of investment worth."

[21] See especially J. Hirshleifer, J. C. DeHaven, and J. W. Milliman, Water Supply, The University of Chicago Press, Chicago, 1960, Chapter 6. The authors estimate the marginal opportunity rate at 10 percent.

[22] This rate is discussed in F. Modigliani and M. H. Miller, "The Cost of Capital, Corporation Finance, and the Theory of Investment," in Solomon, op. cit., pp. 150-81 (reprinted from the American Economic Review, 1958).

A third kind of noticeable deficiency is inadequate diffusion of innovation. Firms may refuse to issue patent licenses to competitors and even harass them with ill-founded infringement suits. New techniques that are unprotected and widely known may spread through the industry with painful slowness.[23] Technology may be developed abroad or in related fields to whose merits our industry remains oblivious.

The fourth kind of deficiency is a failure to arrange for at least one full-time researcher. This is, of course, a dubious standard. It is dubious in part because, when firms, trade associations, or government agencies finance research, they are not responding to market demand or creating any direct use-value. Nevertheless, I have the unsupportable impression that in virtually every kind of economic activity the expected benefit-to-cost ratio for some amount of full-time scientific inquiry now exceeds unity.

The standard is also dubious because almost any amount of research, or under-equipped or pseudo research, is regarded as acceptably different from none at all. The explanation is that I do not see how to specify an optimum amount or mix, but I doubt that actual expenditures will often be excessive. Hence, I resort to specifying merely "at least some."

The only reference to quality is the idea that at least one person should be employed solely for generating ideas. This qualification rests on the impression that freedom from line responsibilities contributes to detachment, continuity and perseverance.

Product Suitability

Bain asserts that, "given some set of known alternatives of design and quality, a fairly clear criterion of ideal product performance in choosing among them is available: Firms should elevate quality...so long as the resulting addition to buyer satisfaction outweighs the resulting addition to cost.... The difficulty is...[that measures] not only of the costs of all...product opportunities, but also of their relative satisfaction-providing power,

---

[23] In contrast, "It took Iowa farmers only four years to go from 10 to 90 percent of their corn acreage in hybrid corn. In areas where the profitability was lower, the adjustment was also slower. On the whole, taking account of uncertainty and the fact that the spread of knowledge is not instantaneous, farmers appear to have behaved in a fashion consistent with the idea of profit maximization." Z. Griliches, "Hybrid Corn: An Exploration in the Economics of Technological Change," Econometrica, October 1957, p. 522.

would be required...." (p. 398). Concerning other aspects of
product performance, too, "there is a simple lack of systematic
factual evidence..." (p. 394).

Bain considers his optimality criterion "not particularly
ambiguous in any essential way" (p. 398). Perhaps, however, it
could use some elaboration for the case where buyers' tastes and
budgets differ.

I presume that there it means choosing the level of quality
(or frequency of product change or degree of variety) and the associated cost, that together maximize buyers' aggregate compensating variation. This meaning weights each buyer's preferences
according to his alternative consumer surpluses. Another possible meaning is some form of direct ballot, with each buyer
having an equal opportunity to rate the alternatives. Either meaning, however, as Bain says, is "terribly difficult to apply to actual cases" (p. 398).

Even so, there may remain some operational standards. I
have three in mind.

Proposition one is that sellers should not suppress product
inventions — for example, by buying and impounding a fruit juice
process that could utilize culls or could be employed in competing
regions.

Proposition two is that sellers should not persistently offer
less than the maximum quality that is available for a given cost.
The evaluation will be adverse if sellers have accidentally or
deliberately debased quality — for example, by reducing durability
at the time of production or by ceasing to offer replacement parts
later on, in order to increase replacement sales.[24] The evaluation will be adverse if sellers have gone to special expense to
reduce serviceability — for example, by fashion changes or by
adding arsenic to a plastic that dentists might substitute for a
more costly material. The evaluation will also be adverse if
sellers have promoted useless, harmful or hazardous products —
for example, false remedies, contaminated foods or appliances
that give lethal shocks.

To apply this standard may not be terribly difficult. It need
not even involve first-hand investigation. Product evaluations
are published monthly in Consumer Reports and Consumers Research. Product tests are conducted or obtained by a number of
government agencies (notably the Bureau of Standards, the Food
and Drug Administration and the Federal Trade Commission).
Numerous deficiencies are alleged in published sources.[25]

---

[24] Concerning the light bulb incident, see G. W. Stocking and M. W. Watkins,
Cartels in Action, The Twentieth Century Fund, New York, 1946, esp. p. 358.
   [25] See, for example, R. A. Brady, Organization, Automation, and Society, University of California Press, Berkeley, 1961, pp. 331-34.

Proposition three is that worthless and troublesome differences among sellers' offerings should not persist. The issue
here is the other side of what is usually regarded as the problem
of an appropriate balance between variety and cost.

With the latter, the question is whether a reduction (or an increase) in the number of designs is possible whose economy (or
whose closer adaptation to the tastes of certain buyers) would
outweigh its disadvantage in reduction of alternatives (or in cost).
Implicit in this question is the idea that an increase in the number of alternatives benefits at least one buyer.

Proliferation of alternatives in some respects, however, will
be detrimental to all buyers. These respects are products and
product attributes concerning which taste differences are irrelevant. Instances may include many drugs, the size of light-bulb
sockets and the meaning of clothing sizes. The respects include
also products and attributes concerning which taste differences
are relevant, but for which continuous variation creates differences below any person's threshold of discrimination. Examples
here may be cleanser strengths, book sizes and construction
modules.[26] Uncoordinated variation in these respects simply
creates confusion and enhances costs of production, exchange and
maintenance.

The question at issue, then, is the extent to which appropriate
standardization has been accomplished.[27] If we distinguish this
question from the question of an appropriate variety-cost balance,
it may appear that we are "lacking in sufficient systematic data,
on the character of buyer preference patterns or on the actual
alternatives of design... and their... costs" (Bain, p. 401), only
for the variety issue.[28]

---

[26] Brady, after thirty years of research concerning standards, writes, "Suppose
all consumers' goods and services were to be classified...|.. About half would be
strictly of a utility character and hence wholly subject to standards procedures;
about one-quarter would have important consumer-preference components, but of
such a character that demand could be satisfied almost entirely from standard products; the remaining quarter, though subject to highly individual preference, would
still have important features to which standards could be applied." Op. cit., p. 334.
Concerning production inputs, the first category presumably would be even broader.

[27] That is, uniformity or controlled variation of definitions, abbreviations, sym-
bols, forms, methods of test, ratings, grades, measures, physical and chemical
properties, designs, sizes, shapes, parts, lubricants, jointly-usable apparatus, containers and ancillary terms of exchange. An interesting application in agriculture is
the limitation of San Joaquin Valley cotton production to Acala 4-42.

[28] A classic study in the field is S. Chase, The Tragedy of Waste, The Macmillan
Co., New York, 1925, pp. 167-74. Current analysis can be found in various publications of the American Standards Association.

Profit Rates

According to Bain:

> Since losses are ideally a penalty imposed by the market to force an efficient adjustment of supply to demand... net losses are undesirable mainly when both... the losses are prolonged... [and] adjustment of supply to demand is not forced through... reduction of... capacity.... (p. 371) Such chronic losses... reflect a failure of the... market mechanism... and... inequities [to] enterprise owners.... (p. 372)
>
> Excess profits to industries should normally be periodic or sporadic. ... Chronic excess profits are at least <u>prima facie</u> suspect of resulting from simple monopolistic restriction.... (p. 378) [If] high excess profits for industries are strongly associated with characteristics of market structure (especially high seller concentration and high barriers to new entry) which would theoretically be expected to head to chronic monopolistic excess profits... we then have some reason to believe... observed excess profits are in considerable part actually monopolistic.... (p. 386) Such profits... result in a larger share of the national income going to enterprise owners, who in general are relatively few and relatively wealthy... and reflect a distortion of the allocation of resources among uses without giving society anything in return. (pp. 371, 377)

This dual standard represents a sophisticated way to recognize both tendencies identified by economic theory and complications encountered in empirical application. It does, however, raise some questions.

Let us consider first the asserted undesirability of certain prolonged losses. To deal with the substantive issues, let us suppose that the losses are not a result of debatable accounting. That is, they remain even after conversion to LIFO, slowing of depreciation, inclusion of total common costs, inclusion of capital gains, revaluation of owned inputs, exclusion of capitalized profits, omission of "pleasant" expenses and voluntary income transfers, correction for a lower price level and use of a period that starts and ends at cyclical peaks.

Even so, it is not obvious that the combination of prolonged losses and excess capacity implies a failure to achieve an appropriate reallocation of resources. The combination may reflect a willingness of many people to receive low rates (or even amounts) of profit in order to be their own bosses or to engage in a particular kind of work. Or it may reflect an optimistic willingness to undertake statistically unsound ventures. It is not clear on what grounds an observer should say that society should decline the gamble or regret the results. The opposite view would also seem to be tenable, particularly if the observer values freedom of choice or if he has the values to which it is relevant that "enterprise owners... in general are relatively wealthy."

Suppose, however, that the combination does indeed imply misallocation. Perhaps this judgment is warranted if the situation reflects ignorance, stupidity, inertia or captivity. In this event, the failure would seem to lie in the excess capacity, not in the losses. Because of their therapeutic effect, the losses would seem to be desirable. Their nonoccurrence would tend to aggravate the allocation problem by reducing the pressure to evacuate.

Asserting that the losses are appropriate would not condone the excess capacity. The excess would be bemoaned under the heading of efficiency or output. Dividing the issues in this way seems not only clearer but also safer. The danger involved is illustrated by the early New Deal recovery measures, some of whose re-enactments are still quite costly. People became oriented to symptoms instead of causes. They even attempted to manipulate the symptoms in a way that aggravated the ailment.

I may, however, be overlooking another danger. Bain asserts that "a basic return equal to the normal interest rate is necessary, 'on the average and in the long-run,' for the maintenance of production by any... group of firms" or for "the enterprise system... [to] work well, in the long-run" (p. 370). The basis for this assertion, however, is not clear to me. By certain calculations, American agriculture has persistently received less than an interest return and yet, aside from a high birth rate, performed well in certain respects, especially in progressiveness.

But even if therapeutic losses are desirable, how large should they be? It is difficult to offer anything significant here. The losses should be large enough to induce reallocation, and "reasonably promptly." It would, of course, be desirable for this minimum to be made small by public policies that facilitate mobility. On the other hand, the losses should not be so large or the reallocation so sudden as to cause the most efficient firms (as well as the inefficient ones) to fail, or to cause insolvency to spread to unwarned suppliers or creditors, or to cause released resources to suffer prolonged idleness.[29] In a word, the losses should be "moderate."

Let us turn now to the asserted undesirability of certain prolonged profits.

---

[29] Compare J. M. Clark, Guideposts in Time of Change, Harper and Brothers, New York, 1949, pp. 144-45.

Prolonged Profits

To deal with the substantive issues, let us suppose that it is indisputable that industry profits represent a return higher than "the" interest rate. This means several things. Every arbitrary accounting decision is resolved in favor of showing smaller profits. The profits are calculated over all sellers in the "industry," including ones with losses and ones who perished, and over a period including the set-up years, when losses were incurred. And the effect of financial leverage on the rate base (but not on taxes) is neutralized by expressing profits, after taxes and after a maximum reasonable charge for interest on net worth, as a ratio to assets, not to net worth. Even so, there are some problems in asserting that the combination of prolonged profits plus high seller concentration and entry barriers is undesirable.

The conclusion that the combination is undesirable derives from a fundamental proposition that I suppose none of us doubts (even though I am aware of no empirical evidence that supports it). The proposition is that in certain market situations sellers will persistently extract unusual and substantial profits even though they do nothing unusual (innovate, etc.), that would in some sense justify the profits. Unusual rates of return can be extracted — and therefore will be extracted — simply because demand, costs and the nature of competition create favorable opportunities for gain.

A sufficient set of conditions for such unjustifiable profits apparently is enlightened self-interest, adequate demand relative to costs, weak countervailing power, high-entry barriers and an adequate deterrent to profit-lowering internal expansion of capacity (in the form of diseconomies of scale or of fewness of sellers — the latter, taken in conjunction with enlightened self-interest, implying oligopolistic anticipation of struggle or monopolistic adjustment to opportunities).

There is a difficulty in applying the undoubted proposition empirically. It is that none of the mentioned sufficient conditions is incompatible with circumstances whose occurrence is commonly regarded as a justification of positive profits (as well as an additional cause, or substitute sufficient condition, of positive profits). Four such circumstances may be mentioned: socially useful innovation, unusually favorable cost performance, market expansion and investing despite an unusually high likelihood of calamities (calamities that have not yet occurred and hence have not yet been reflected in actual returns).[30]

---

[30]Like Bain (p. 377), I do not agree with the common assertion that reinvestment is an additional justification of profits. To persuade me, I think it would be necessary

In fact, at least one of these four circumstances commonly —
perhaps invariably — is present. Certainly patented and unpatented
product improvement is a frequent occurrence. In particular, it
is a prominent feature in industries, such as automobile manufacturing, that apparently have persistently received relatively
high profits.[31]

The concurrence of extenuating circumstances creates difficulties because no plausible and reasonably precise standards
seem to be available that indicate how large or how long-lived a
return the circumstances justify. As a result, when any of the
extenuating circumstances is present, there seems to be little
basis for asserting that actual returns are greater than can be
justified. To be sure, risk cannot justify returns that exceed the
interest rate by more than about 100 percent of investment per investment period. And innovation, economizing and reallocation
cannot justify profits that exceed the social gains. These, however, are rather high limits.

Considering this problem, Bain asserts that "excess profits
to industries should...[be] sporadic (as windfall, risk, and innovation reward would make them)" (p. 378). Aside from why the
profits both should be and would be sporadic, the meaning of
"sporadic" and of "innovation" is not clear to me. Certainly
there is no magic in a notion such as whatever proceeds a patentee — and only a patentee — can extract during pendency plus
two apprenticeships plus three years.

In practice, consequently, it appears that there is commonly
— perhaps invariably — an inadequate basis for asserting that prolonged profits are unjustifiable if combined with high-seller concentration and entry barriers, or with the sufficient set of

---

to show that: (1) Most profits are reinvested, (2) greater (ex ante) investment would
be socially desirable, (3) firms with opportunities to extract profits would direct
capital into the socially best uses, (4) otherwise-justified profits and implicit interest are inadequate, (5) capital markets are excessively costly, (6) customers should
provide the capital on which owners receive a return, (7) owners seldom sell and
convert wealth into consumption, (8) nonreinvestment justifies losses and (9) the
directors of "200" giant corporations should make decisions that could be left to the
impersonal market or to the stockholders.

Concerning the last, I favor the proposal to make discretionary cash dividends
deductible from taxable income for all corporations, instead of merely for "exempt"
cooperatives. The effects would include reducing double taxation and increasing
corporate payout ratios. Higher payout ratios would lessen the transformation of
ordinary income into capital gains and — most relevant — restore the decision on reinvestment of earnings to stockholders.

[31] For present purposes it does not matter whether or not the extenuating circumstances are found disproportionately in conjunction with high concentration and entry
barriers. Some generalizations are beginning to emerge on this subject, particularly
from the work of Carter and Williams; Jewkes, Sawers, and Stillerman; Maclaurin;
Mueller; Nutter; Sanders; Schmookler; Stigler; Worley; and the Senate Committee on
the Judiciary.

conditions mentioned above. Given these conditions, it is true, unjustifiable profits apparently would have occurred even in the absence of the extenuating circumstances, and actual profits apparently have been enlarged with them. Nevertheless, unjustifiability does not follow unless there are no circumstances acceptable as extenuating, or none of the extenuating circumstances is present, or those present can be shown not to justify profits as large as have occurred.

On the other hand, it equally does not follow that observed returns, however high, are justifiable if innovation, etc., has occurred at some time. Justification derives from the idea that it is socially advantageous to provide rewards and therefore incentives to innovators, cost-cutters, demand satisfiers and risk bearers. If this idea implies that it is justifiable for them to capture all the available gains from trade, however, it loses some cogency.

Alternatives

The double non sequitur seems to leave two alternatives. One is to admit that there is little basis for saying that prolonged profits are either justified or unjustified when any extenuating circumstances are present. The other is to formulate some guidelines that are admittedly imperfect but nevertheless at least do identify many extreme cases of unjustifiable returns without also misidentifying many cases of justifiable returns. I would like to pursue the second alternative, but I do not have any tolerable guidelines.

Suppose, however, that criteria were available that would indicate how much of observed profits were justifiable, or — to take a clearer case — that prolonged profits occur with no extenuating circumstances present. Suppose, that is, that unjustifiable profits can be identified. Does it follow that they should be condemned? Are profits that are unjustifiable also undesirable, not merely neutral?

Undesirability, not mere neutrality, is asserted by Bain and others on the grounds of a contribution to misallocation of resources and to inequitable distribution of income.

The misallocation argument appears to involve the following contention: unjustifiable profits seldom will occur unless accompanied by undesirable restriction of quantity sold, and undesirable restriction will seldom be warranted by concomitant advantages (such as redistribution or financial self-sufficiency) if it is accompanied by unjustifiable profits.

This contention appears to follow if a number of statements of fact and judgments of value are accepted. One of the former may be the following: in most industries that receive unjustifiable profits, an average ratio of price to marginal private cost over the industry's sellers and products is greater than an average ratio over the sellers and products whose outputs would decrease if our industry's prices were lower.[32]

I single out this condition because I suppose that it is a necessary condition and the one whose accuracy is most questionable. I am not aware of any evidence that has been offered to support it.

Its accuracy would, of course, follow tautologically if competing industries were in purely competitive static equilibrium while our industry had marginal costs no greater than average costs and therefore less than prices. But this contrast does not necessarily follow even if there are numerous sellers in all competing industries and one seller in our industry, and it seems to follow even less if all that is said is that there are high concentration and entry barriers in our industry. Among other things, the competing industries may be receiving profits that are justified by innovation.

The importance of the condition, it is true, can be avoided by arguing that if ratios of price to marginal cost are above unity in competing industries, they too should be lowered. It is not clear to me that this argument is relevant in appraising performance in individual markets.

The redistribution argument also appears to follow if a number of statements of fact and judgments of value are accepted. One of the former may be the following: reduction of unjustifiable profits would not be a disadvantage to new owners who bought into the firms at inflated security prices.[33]

---

[32] Additional conditions might include the following: (2) Ratios of marginal social cost to marginal private cost for the industry are no greater than for competing industries. (3) If prices were lower, quantity sold would be greater (in broadcasting?). (4) Buyers' demand for the product should be respected (despite ignorance, sales promotion, the nature of the commodity, and the distribution of purchasing power). (5) It is desirable to make a change that enhances the welfare of the industry's actual and potential customers by enough for them to overcompensate those who suffer (e.g., competing industries) even though the latter in fact are not compensated. (6) Unjustifiable profits would be eliminated by lowering prices, not by raising them, by raising production costs or by intensifying advertising.

[33] Additional conditions might include the following: (2) Profits in the industry do not enhance investors' optimism enough to reduce the economy-wide level of profits received by wealthy people. (3) The beneficiaries of the industry's profits are extremely wealthy people, and the profits would be eliminated in a way that would enhance disproportionately the wealth or real incomes of middlemen or consumers who are extremely poor people, as that elimination would unambiguously reduce inequality of purchasing power. (Incidentally, a lower input price to a purely competitive industry is not necessarily an advantage. It can lead to expansion of output in the face of an inelastic demand and cause industry profits to end up smaller.)

The relevance of this condition may not be apparent. It stems from the view that a case for avoiding creation of unjustifiable incomes does not constitute a case for destroying them after new owners have paid for them.[34] After unjustifiable profits have been capitalized in security prices, they represent unjustified incomes only in the sense that income from other purchased property represents that. The assertion that one aggravates inequality applies equally to the other. If this justifies condemning one, it would appear also to justify condemning the other. Reduction of either, however, implies disappointment of a kind usually regarded as unfair.

I am not aware that it has been shown that capitalization would not occur or that reduction of unjustifiable profits would occur before capitalization.

Nevertheless, I accept the redistribution argument if it applies — that is, if the owners are wealthy — and regardless of whether concentration and entry barriers are high. I do so because unjustifiable profits are a form of property income whose reduction could be especially easy, and because reduction of unjustifiable profits could alter inequality in a way that appeals to my prejudices. These are not very compelling reasons.

Furthermore, I have the impression that reduction of unjustifiable profits would not materially alter the distribution of purchasing power. Bain estimates (p. 384) that the adjusted after-tax excess profits of all American incorporated and unincorporated businesses amount to 2.0-3.5 percent of national income. These are excess profits only in the sense that imputed interest has already been subtracted, not innovation rewards, etc. After subtracting the latter, we would have the unjustified remainder.

The amount to subtract is, of course, uncertain. An indication, however, is provided by Bain's study of the correlation of profit rates with seller concentration. His coefficient of determination for a linear fit was 0.11.[35] From this, one might infer that

---

(4) Reduced inequality is desirable. (5) Inequality can be altered significantly by eliminating unjustifiable profits. (6) Elimination would not replace better ways of accomplishing redistribution. (7) The advantages of smaller inequality would not be outweighed by reduced employee benefits, reduced research, reduced investment, reduced tax payments, added costs of external financing and problems associated with the method of eliminating the profits.

[34] Compare D. Dewey, Monopoly in Economics and Law, Rand McNally & Co., Chicago, 1959, Chapter 17.

[35] J. S. Bain, "Relation of Profit Rate to Industry Concentration: American Manufacturing, 1936-40," Quarterly Journal of Economics, August 1951, pp. 293-324. See also: J. S. Bain, Barriers to New Competition, Harvard University Press, Cambridge, 1956, pp. 190-201; V. R. Fuchs, "Integration, Concentration, and Profits in Manufacturing Industries," Quarterly Journal of Economics, May 1961, pp. 278-91; L. F. Schrader and N. R. Collins, "Relation of Profit Rates to Industry Structure in the Food Industries," Journal of Farm Economics, December 1960, pp. 1526-27; L. W. Weiss, Economics and American Industry, John Wiley & Sons, New York, 1961, Chapter 11.

unjustified profits amount to something under 1.0 percent of national income. In any event, it seems that as Bain observes "Total elimination of all excess profits would not change the national distribution of income, or the average relation of prices to costs, very much" (p. 384).

Unjustified Losses

The other side of unjustifiable profits is unjustifiable losses. Following my earlier discussion of therapeutic losses, these would be losses not accompanied by excess capacity or other mistakes. If not, the losses presumably would seldom be persistent, although one can imagine instances of frequent miscalculation, price war or exercise of buyers' bargaining power. The most common situation might involve capacities adjusted to peak demands, marginal costs usually below average costs and prices often falling toward marginal costs.

When losses result from marginal-cost pricing, it is not easy to support a contention that the losses imply misallocation.

Another contention might be that the losses imply unfair disappointment to the (original) owners — inequities, as Bain put it. Disappointment here, in contrast with the case of deliberate reduction of capitalized profits, strikes me as a risk of the venturer, not as an inequity.

My inclination, consequently, is to react to unjustified losses as I react to unjustified profits: They are undesirable if they aggravate inequality, or if they interfere with continued production or with efficiency or progress — this interference being an additional possibility in the case of losses.[36]

In sum, my reaction to multi-year industry-wide profit rates is as follows: (1) Moderate losses, when accompanied by excess capacity or other mistakes, are desirable. (2) Immoderate losses are undesirable. (3) Also undesirable are losses not accompanied by mistakes if the losses contribute to inequality or if they interfere with good performance in other respects. (4) Otherwise, such unaccompanied losses are neither desirable nor undesirable. (5) Positive profits accompanied by innovation, cost-cutting, market expansion or (true) risk justification are neither desirable nor undesirable, except that such accompanied profits are undesirable if they both exceed a justifiable level (if such can be determined) and contribute to inequality. (6) Profits not so

---

[36] That returns below an interest rate may accrue to relatively wealthy people is illustrated in certain segments of American agriculture.

accompanied are undesirable if they contribute to inequality or to perpetuation of excess capacity. (7) Otherwise, such unaccompanied profits are neither desirable nor undesirable. (8) The observer should not be so distracted by profit rates that he neglects the important aspects of performance.

Level of Output

Because unjustifiable profits may not imply undesirable restriction of output and because the level of output may be objectionable without being accompanied by unjustifiable profits, it seems appropriate to refer to output directly. This is, of course, the standard procedure in welfare theory.

From welfare theory has come the norm that, for each product, marginal (social) cost should equal product price and, for each input, (social) value of marginal product should equal input price. The norm is not applicable to a particular industry, however, if in other industries it is violated in varying and unknown degrees. Violation implies that input prices and product marginal costs do not represent social opportunity costs. In this case, welfare theory appears merely to suggest that there should be a "reasonable relation" between marginal cost and product price and between value of marginal product and input price.

This suggestion, nevertheless, contains a number of nontrivial propositions. Four pertain to underproduction.

One is that output is insufficient if it is needlessly reduced by a positive price when marginal social cost equals zero. This is probably the most acceptable practicable conclusion of welfare economics. It is the only case where the argument for equality of marginal cost and price is independent of conditions in other industries, since there is no reduction of other production to be weighed against the advantages of increased output in one industry.

Even so, there are at least four qualifications. This is why I included the word "needlessly." First of all, distribution effects are involved.[37] Second, marginal taxation may be used to finance the supplying institution, with accompanying distortion of various prices. Third, decisions as to indivisible changes in producing

---

[37] The item is to be provided free to persons who otherwise would have paid for it. There is a loss of revenues to the institution making the item available. There is a shift in the burden of finance. There may be external effects on producers of substitutes and complements. If nothing else, there will be a change in relative status and therefore the question of envy.

the item may be made more difficult by lack of a market test. Finally, there may be difficulties concerning overutilization.[38]

Of course, "Examples of pure public goods are few."[39] Nevertheless, if one is at issue, it seems to me appropriate to expect a zero price unless there are good reasons to the contrary. It does not strike me as a good reason that this price would be inconsistent with unsubsidized private enterprise. The fact that a particular institution will not give good performance in certain situations does not seem to me a sufficient reason for redefining good performance.

A second proposition is that industry output is insufficient if it is reduced by prices that could be lowered without lowering industry profits, or if less has been produced than could be sold at a marginal revenue above marginal cost. The larger output seems preferable because it implies an increase in both consumers' and producers' surplus; the increase should be large enough to overcompensate producers and consumers who would suffer from lower prices in our industry; and this suffering should be disregarded on grounds of consumers' sovereignty.

The availability of price reductions that do not reduce profits is not something one hears about when certainty has been assumed. In practice, however, it may result from miscalculation of demand and costs, from having a high-cost price-leader, from fear of price wars and from public controls. Concerning a phase of the latter, Bain comments that regulatory commissions "cannot insist that a much larger output and lower rate be made available on the theory that costs would also be covered at the larger output" (p. 598).

A third proposition is that output is insufficient if it would be greater at lower prices and if ratios of price to short-run marginal (social) cost regularly are greater than in identifiable competing industries. The idea here is that there are industries whose output would diminish if our industry expanded output. It is from these industries that our industry's additional inputs would come, if only indirectly. The social cost of additional output in our industry then is the value of the output that the additional inputs would have produced in those competing industries.

---

[38] Overutilization problems do not arise where supply is inexhaustible, as in broadcasting and beacons, or where demand is sufficiently constrained, as in sewage disposal. But they do arise where increasing use at some point implies deprivation or discomfort for other users, as in museums, parks, concerts, roads, bridges and conveyances. In such cases a positive price may be warranted, despite frequent needless exclusion. The alternative is to have price uncertain, to leave the decision to doorkeepers, and to encourage people to tarry on the chance of last-minute free admission.

[39] F. M. Bator, The Question of Government Spending, Harper & Brothers, New York, 1960, p. 95.

This value of marginal product may differ from the inputs' cost. Hence marginal cost in our industry should be adjusted to reflect the difference. The adjustment factor is the ratios of price to marginal cost in the competing industries. Suppose they can be identified and their ratios calculated. If the ratios are predominantly less than ratios in our industry, then increased output in our industry would create more value than it would destroy.

Fourth, output is (ultimately, though not necessarily immediately) insufficient if it would be greater at lower prices and if ratios of price to long-run marginal (social) cost regularly are greater than in identifiable competing industries. In other words, even if there are acceptably low ratios of price to short-run marginal cost in our industry, output is insufficient if fixed inputs should be enlarged and prices lowered toward the new lower levels of short-run marginal cost.

Concerning the fixed inputs, we can say that they should be enlarged if short-run marginal costs chronically exceed long-run marginal costs over the range of outputs usually experienced. In this event, capacity is not large enough to minimize total costs, since short-run marginal cost is less than, equal to or greater than long-run marginal cost according to whether output is less than, equal to or greater than the level at which the capacity being utilized would minimize total costs.

Concerning prices, we can say that they should be lower if ratios of price to <u>appropriate</u> short-run marginal cost (equal to long-run marginal cost) in our industry chronically exceed ratios of price to actual short-run marginal cost for competing industries. These are the industries whose output would be curtailed if prices were lower in our industry; and we must be able to identify the industries, calculate their ratios and compare them to the potential ratios in our industry.

Overproduction

Three reciprocal propositions pertain to overproduction.

First, output is excessive if usually more is produced than can be sold at prices as high as short-run marginal costs, or if output would be smaller at higher prices and prices regularly are less than short-run marginal costs. This sort of overproduction is unprofitable. It may, however, result from miscalculations, price wars and public controls. It may be condemned on the assumption that prices elsewhere are at least as great as marginal costs. If so, releasing some inputs from our industry should decrease value of output in our industry by less than it increases value of output elsewhere.

Second and closely related, output is excessive if the value of a movable input's marginal product regularly is clearly less than its expected value in other uses. This sort of overproduction may result from mispriced inputs, from immobility and from an institutional conversion of socially variable into privately fixed costs.

Sometimes the price of an input to our industry clearly may be less than the value of output that it could produce elsewhere. Alternatively, the input may be owner-supplied and its imputed return be less than its price elsewhere. In either situation, marginal social cost exceeds marginal private cost. If so, product price should exceed marginal private cost. Equality between the two would be equivalent to an excess of marginal cost over product price where input prices are taken at face value. The latter is the situation condemned in the previous proposition. Here, however, a particular input is identified as excessive.

Schultz stressed labor when he argued "that more than half of the labor force devoted to farming has an output (value productivity) less than half the standard output of comparable human resources in the American economy taken as a whole." [40]

Third, output is (ultimately, though not necessarily immediately) excessive if it would be smaller at higher prices and if prices regularly are less than long-run marginal costs. In other words, even if there are relatively high ratios of price to short-run marginal cost in our industry, output is excessive if fixed inputs should be reduced and prices raised toward the new, higher levels of short-run marginal cost. And we can say that capacity should be reduced if long-run marginal costs chronically exceed short-run marginal costs over the range of outputs usually experienced.

The seven propositions leave a large gap. They say nothing about what is presumably the typical situation outside of agricultural production: prices exceed short-run and long-run marginal (social) costs; but marginal costs are positive, lower prices would not increase profits and ratios of price to marginal cost in competing industries cannot be identified, measured or compared with those in our industry. Unfortunately, I do not see how to close this gap.

---

[40] T. W. Schultz, Production and Welfare of Agriculture, The Macmillan Co., New York, 1949, p. 61. The reverse situation probably exists in industries where wage rates are unusually high. The result then, however, is not necessarily insufficient output relative to competing industries. To be sure, this conclusion does seem to follow where high wage rates are conjoined with part-time work, as in coal mining. Even there, however, it is not clear whether one should say that output is too small or labor is too immobile.

I have the impression, however, that it is not a serious omission. I have the impression that the social losses resulting from discrepancies between actual and ideal product prices are close to negligible. This is not to say that the composition of social output appears to me unimportant. It would not long be a happy situation if only ice cream were produced. But more than ice cream would be produced even if there were static perfect competition in ice cream production and static monopoly in everything else. The relevant question is the importance of marginal discrepancies attributable to profiteering.

Harberger has estimated that the aggregate welfare loss associated with misallocation in the manufacturing sector (which originates about 30 percent of national income) may amount to 0.1 percent of national income.[41] Perhaps then it is true that "It is not [price, quality, promotional] competition which counts but the competition from the new technology, the new source of supply, the new type of organization. . . . [This kind is] so much more important that it becomes a matter of comparative indifference whether competition in the ordinary sense functions more or less promptly; the powerful lever that in the long-run expands output and brings down prices is in any case made of other stuff."[42]

Exchange Efficiency

What seems to me to constitute desirable functioning of the process of exchange can be expressed in seven propositions.

Proposition one is that transportation costs should not persistently be needlessly large. The qualification "persistently" is intended to make allowance for "reasonable" lags in adjustment.

Sometimes excessive transportation is readily ascertainable and even quantifiable. This will be true when a "central market" sits outside the location polygon. It will be true when firms continually ship perfect substitutes into each other's "natural" market areas.[43] It will be true when route duplication occurs.[44] It will be true when needlessly frequent small shipments occur.[45]

---

[41] A. C. Harberger, "Monopoly and Resource Allocation," American Economic Review, May 1954, p. 86. See also D. Schwartzman, "The Burden of Monopoly," Journal of Political Economy, December 1960, p. 627.

[42] J. A. Schumpeter, Capitalism, Socialism, and Democracy, 3rd edition, Harper & Row, New York, 1950, pp. 84-85.

[43] For examples of asserted cross-hauling, see Brady, op. cit., p. 340.

[44] See particularly R. G. Bressler, Jr., City Milk Distribution, Harvard University Press, Cambridge, 1952, Part 2.

[45] "If farmers in Nebraska purchased farm supplies in minimum quantities of 5-tons of fertilizer, 1-ton of feed, and 300-gallons of petroleum, and from the retailer nearest their farms, costs of retailing and delivery could be reduced by at

It will also be true when outlets are concentrated although customers rarely survey the alternatives (as with gasoline) and when outlets are scattered although comparative shopping is common (as with furniture). At other times production adjustments should be considered simultaneously, by comparing the cost of actual shipments with the cost of "A set of nonnegative delivery levels which minimizes the total costs of extraction and transportation." [46]

Proposition two is that economical facilities should exist at assembly points. [47]

Proposition three is that price formation and the pairing of buyers and sellers should not be unreasonably costly. It is difficult to suggest what is unreasonable here, although needless costs, of course, are included. The difficulty does not, I think, imply that there are no problems or no ways to evaluate them in practice.

Haggling is only a century gone in the United States and then only in certain types of merchandising. In other fields an unreasonable number of free estimates is often solicited. For many used or unique items, a central listing service is yet to be developed. Where auctions are used, a Dutch auction could be cheaper per unit sold than an ordinary auction. [48] Where bids are submitted, the presence of rules of trading that make the price that a successful bidder pays (as well as his success) depend on his own bid, encourages expensive espionage, mental strain and frustration. (See proposition seven below for an alternative.)

Proposition four is that price flexibility should not generate costly search for information, needless livelihoods for speculators or inefficient accommodation to uncertainty. The last is one of the arguments for "Forward Prices for Agriculture."

Proposition five is that prices should be high enough to avoid excess demand and low enough to avoid undesired inventory accumulation. Excess demand leads to queues, favoritism and extramarginal purchases. Undesired inventory accumulation leads

---

least $2.2 million, or 12.4 percent." R. G. Walsh and K. R. Erlewine, "Pricing Efficiency of Farm Supply Cooperatives," Extension and Research Workshops on Farmer Cooperatives (Supplement to American Cooperation 1961), p. 67. The authors assert that much of the inefficiency "could be corrected by a system of quantity discount pricing," (ibid., p. 69).

In the same vein, see D. A. Clarke, Jr., Milk Delivery Costs and Volume Pricing Procedures in California, California Agricultural Experiment Station Bulletin 757 (1956).

[46] J. M. Henderson, The Efficiency of the Coal Industry, Harvard University Press, Cambridge, 1958, p. 113.

[47] The congestion, lack of loading platforms, etc., that exists at many urban produce centers is notorious. See for example, W. T. Calhoun, H. E. Erdman, and G. L. Mehren, Improving the San Francisco Wholesale Fruit and Vegetable Market, U. S. Bureau of Economics, Washington, D. C., Berkeley, 1943, and the literature cited in G. S. Shepherd, Marketing Farm Products, 3rd edition, Iowa State University Press, Ames, 1955, p. 468.

[48] See G. E. Riddell, "Farmers in Low Countries Sell by the Clock," News for Farmer Cooperatives, September 1950, pp. 3, 21.

to problems well known to agricultural economists. Either result represents an extreme failure in the next respect to be mentioned, which will need greater elaboration.

Proposition six is that, for a set of prospective buyers and sellers at an assembly point, the ratio of actual to potential gains from trade should be maximized. The gains from trade can be measured by the sum (over all persons who contract to buy or sell) of the maximum amount of money that — if the contracts were to be fulfilled — each would be able to give up without putting himself in a position that he would prefer less than if the contracts were to be annulled. The amount of money involved for any participant if there are no external diseconomies represents the variation in his cash position that would exactly compensate for performance of his contracts. It would compensate in the sense that, if he would need to pay the amount (perhaps in attorney's fees) to secure performance, he would be indifferent whether or not the contracts had been made (provided that the trouble of making them would be reimbursed).

Empirical quantification of this measure requires learning four things. First, it requires learning what contracts actually were made. Second, it requires learning the gains from trade that are associated with the actual contracts. This involves ascertaining for each person who contracted to buy (or sell) the largest (or smallest) amount that he could pay (or accept) for his units of the commodity without putting himself in a position that he would prefer less than acquiring (or unloading) no units. Third, it requires learning the contracts that would have maximized the gains from trade. These contracts are the intramarginal, or perfectly competitive, transactions.[49] Even with bilateral atomism present,

---

[49] That perfect competition will — more exactly, is defined to — produce the intramarginal transactions does not imply that its performance in other respects would be desirable, that it is attainable, or that — as Clark pointed out — any of its structural attributes would be desirable unless all are present (J. M. Clark, "Toward a Concept of Workable Competition," American Economic Review, June 1940, pp. 241-56). I refer to perfect competition here simply because it is an easy way, with an audience of economists, to clarify what transactions are intramarginal and what is the intersection price. The norm being presented is in no way "shored up" by the notion or desirability of perfect competition.

Furthermore, it now appears that the structure and conduct ordinarily thought to produce an outcome consisting of the intramarginal transactions are in fact neither necessary nor sufficient, and in any event include unmanageable concepts such as perfect knowledge. (See the literature cited in H. Uzawa, "Walras' Tatonnement in the Theory of Exchange," Review of Economic Studies, June 1960, p. 194.)

Instead, these four attributes may be mentioned as a sufficient set of conditions: No collusive communication, a homogeneous commodity, negligible interest of any participant in a second unit and rules of trading that prescribe sale of all units simultaneously either by ordinary auction or by bilateral sealed bids, with all prices to equal the highest rejected bid. In these circumstances all participants confront

the intramarginal transactions can, and apparently often will,[50] differ from the actual transactions, unless individual prices during a market session equal the average price and the average price equals the price (or, with indivisibilities, the range of price) given by intersection of demand and supply. Fourth, it requires learning what gains from trade would have been associated with intramarginal transactions.

These four pieces of information are in principle obtainable. It should be possible to obtain good approximations by conducting interviews and/or tests with the participants. In practice, however, the process would be too expensive and too time-consuming to be undertaken more than, at best, occasionally.

The practical obstacles do not make the norm irrelevant. Certain market characteristics appear needlessly to reduce the expected value of the measure. Hence the norm can serve one of the functions of performance norms — namely, implying norms for structure and conduct dimensions — even though it is seldom quantified itself.

One implication is the traditional condemnation of price discrimination administered by sellers. Two other implications are of recent origin.

Chamberlin has shown that "If, instead of trading continuously in the stock market (for example), buyers and sellers submitted bids and offers hourly to a central authority who would arrange them in schedules and announce the equilibrium price, the volume of sales would be substantially reduced without (it would appear) greatly interfering with anyone's legitimate purchases or sales. ..."[51]

Similarly, Vickrey has shown that:

...in the sale of a number of identical items, say an issue of bonds, on the basis of sealed bids ... [a uniform price not merely avoids discrimination but] has the more material advantage of reducing the probability that a bidder's own bid will affect the price he receives, thus inducing bids closer to the full value to the bidder, improving the chances of obtaining ... the optimum allocation ... and reducing effort and expense devoted to socially superfluous investigation of the general market situation. To obtain these advantages

---

each other, and a uniquely optimal pricing formula containing no indeterminacy — creating reference to others' actions should be obvious to all participants. Compare W. Vickrey, "Counterspeculation, Auctions, and Competitive Sealed Tenders," Journal of Finance, March 1961, p. 24.

[50] For evidence pertaining to a simulated market, see E. H. Chamberlin, Towards a More General Theory of Value, Oxford University Press, New York, 1957, Chapter 11. This is apparently the only empirical test of the law of supply and demand that has been published — an interesting commentary on a supposedly scientific discipline.

[51] Op. cit., p. 247.

in full, however, it is necessary to go one step further than is usually done and make the uniform price to be charged the successful bidders equal to the first bid rejected rather than the last bid accepted. . . .[52]

Proposition seven is that, for a set of geographically scattered prospective buyers and sellers, the ratio of actual to potential gains from trade should be maximized. The principal testable implication here is that average prices for an essentially homogeneous commodity at spatially separated assembly points should not persistently differ by more than unit transportation costs, and should not persistently differ by less than that much if the commodity is actually shipped. A number of valuable studies of locational price differences has recently been made.[53]

Cost of Sales Promotion

Bain writes:

> Selling activities . . . may be grouped under three . . . headings: advertising of all sorts; . . . the use of 'salesmen' . . . as distinguished from . . . clerks . . . ; and increments to distributive services . . . taking the form of unduly numerous outlets and unnecessarily large labor forces. . . . (pp. 388, 393)
> Much of . . . [the nonadvertising] increment to cost is . . . incurred with a persuasive orientation, and [is] socially wasteful. . . . An alternative way of describing the result . . . is to say that the 'product' of distributive facilities . . . (namely, the provision of convenience and service . . .) is made elaborate and expensive. . . . (p. 392) Evaluation . . . is difficult . . . because of doubt concerning the extent to which expensive distribution is economically supplying an actual demand by consumers. . . . For at least some extreme cases, however, a fairly clear abberation from distributive efficiency is present. (p. 393)

I am happy to take the option of regarding lavish distribution as a question of product level. The dilemma seems to be the same, and the presence of promotional intent or persuasive orientation seems inconclusive. Thus, it seems to me, too, that one should ask whether the convenience of having the distance between

---

[52] Op. cit., p. 26.
[53] P. L. Farris, "The Pricing Structure for Wheat at the Country Elevator Level," Journal of Farm Economics, August 1958, pp. 607-24; J. B. Hassler, "Pricing Efficiency in the Manufactured Dairy Products Industry," Hilgardia, August 1953, pp. 235-334; M. E. Juillerat and P. L. Farris, Soybean Pricing and Grading at Indiana Country Elevators and Processing Plants, Purdue University Research Bulletin 700, August 1960; D. A. Storey and P. L. Farris, Corn Price Variations in One Indiana County, Purdue University Research Bulletin 694, May 1960. See also the literature on basing-point pricing.

service stations average (say) one mile instead of two is worth an extra (say) one cent per gallon to enough customers.

But it is also agreeable that, at least in some cases, the issue should be regarded as one of (exchange) efficiency. Whereas the question just posed seems difficult, another seems less so: Is it worth an extra (say) one cent per gallon to have four underutilized stations concentrated at points averaging four miles apart instead of one every two miles?

Concerning advertising, Bain comments:

[A] certain modicum of selling activity and cost devoted to informational purposes are... essential to the effective working of a market system. Persuasive promotion... and its costs are basically wasteful, and more so as they become larger. [A] large proportion of observed promotional activities and costs have, to all appearances, a dominantly persuasive orientation, and this relative emphasis is generally greater as selling costs are larger in proportion to sales. (p. 389)

It is common to industries with

costs equal to five percent or more of sales revenue... that nearly all advertising effort... has a persuasive... orientation. All or most of the industries with relatively high advertising costs are seriously suspect of... [unworkability] in the sense that wasteful promotion costs have exceeded the 'limit of tolerance' or 'margin for error' which should probably be allowed in making normative evaluations.... (p. 391)

The distinction between informative and persuasive advertising is a difficult one to make, and one should proceed from it with caution. The difficulty, however, appears to be merely that it is a matter of degree, and I do not doubt that the distinction can be and should be made. It seems to me reasonable to suggest that all industries now spending more than five percent on advertising have deficient performance.

It is not clear to me, however, why condemnation should be limited to them. One possibility is that costs are outweighed by informational benefits in industries with smaller percentages. This explanation might be inferred from Bain's observation that persuasive orientation is positively correlated with the percentage spent. Probably, however, this is not the explanation, since Bain lists automobiles and petroleum products among the industries with less than five percent. (p. 390)

Another possibility is the idea of a "margin for error." A notion of this sort seems to me appropriate. Suppose, for example, that an observer feels that three percent spent on information would be desirable. Probably he then should refrain from condemning four percent spent on information. The grounds

would be that the optimum amount cannot be determined exactly
or, if known, should not be expected to be attained exactly.

But it is an entirely different thing then to withhold condemnation of four percent spent on persuasion — or three, two or one
percent. One percent strikes me as fully one percent too much if
it can be established as functionless, not to say deceitful. It is, I
grant, only one-fifth as wasteful as five percent. But it seems no
less "suspect" unless it takes five thefts per year to make a thief.

On the other hand, some advertising is informative — particularly advertising announcing unexpected availability or prices.
For informative advertising, limiting acceptability to five percent could be a mistake. Spending ten percent could be too little
if more is needed to convey worthwhile information. I cannot
cite any instances where ten percent is at present well spent.
But this seems to me to prove nothing except perhaps my own
ignorance, since I also cannot cite any instances where two percent is at present well spent. I simply do not know how much
would be spent by firms who were really concerned to be informative (although the communications of cooperatives to members
might be indicative). I suspect that the percentage would vary
widely according to the market situation. If so, a single figure
would be either grossly insufficient for cases where adequate
dissemination is very costly or grossly excessive elsewhere.

A five percent criterion, therefore, seems to me unsatisfactory whether the advertising under consideration is persuasive
or informative. What is needed is benefit-cost analysis. A percentage test seems to me not only an inadequate substitute but a
needless one. To undertake benefit-cost analysis, I would use
three assumptions that I will not attempt to justify here.

First, the social cost of any advertising is measured by its
money cost to the advertiser minus any part thereof that defrays
the nonadvertising costs of publishing and broadcasting. This
assumption implies, most importantly, that the use of advertising
inputs is a social sacrifice, that the advertiser pays for all of the
inputs used, and that the money cost to the advertiser (including
any rents) measures the social value of inputs.

Second, the social benefit of any advertising is measured by
the money value of its text to its audience. By the money value
I mean the sum — over all auditors — of the maximum amount that
each, after learning the facts, would believe he could pay for the
advertising without putting himself in a position that he prefers
less than not having received the message. This assumption implies, most importantly, that any information or entertainment
for which the audience would pay nothing is worthless, that any
savings realized by the audience are to be assessed at full value

regardless of pricing practices, that any gains realized by the advertiser are to be disregarded and that all benefits and burdens not ascribable to textual content cancel out.

Third, an excess of cost over benefit, as just defined, is a generally acceptable criterion of undesirable advertising. This assumption implies, most importantly, that welfare redistribution and interpersonal comparisons are negligible difficulties.

In practice, of course, the benefit will be difficult to estimate.[54] Even when advertisements are sold, they usually form only part of the publication being priced, and more spending units read than buy (and consumer surplus exists for those who do buy).

The difficulty does not disturb me. There seems to be much current advertising for which the cost is positive and the benefit is obviously nonpositive. I refer, of course, to advertising that is purely persuasive or even deceptive. As to advertising whose benefit is unmeasurable but apparently positive, I would simply withhold judgment until an appropriate public policy has been implemented. This policy would consist of a set of measures that does everything reasonably possible to make both deceptive and purely persuasive advertising unprofitable. Thereafter, where quantification is infeasible, I would be content simply to presume that any kind and amount of advertising that is undertaken is desirable.

Unethical Practices

The norm here is that unethical practices should not occur. This was, of course, implicit in the use of the pejorative adjective. The important question is what practices merit the label. Perhaps most of us would agree on the following categories, which derive from English common law: undisclosed danger, fraud, misrepresentation, adulteration, passing off, infringement, espionage, disparagement, molestation, harassment by litigation, sabotage, bribery, inducing breach of contract, lotteries, boycotts and price warring.[55] Possibly price and other forms of discrimination should be added.

---

[54] Estimating the cost, while not easy, appears feasible. Borden's data for 1935 indicate that about 20 percent of the money spent by advertisers ended up, after deducting the costs of carrying advertising, as a net contribution to the nonadvertising costs (or the profits) of the media of public expression. See N. H. Borden, Advertising in Our Economy, Richard D. Irwin, Inc., Chicago, 1945, pp. 19-21.

[55] For the meaning of these words, along with numerous actual cases, see especially R. Callmann, The Law of Unfair Competition and Trade-Marks, 2nd edition, Callaghan, Chicago, 1950, Vols. I and II.

The Printers Ink Model Statute has been adopted with some variations, by most

Participant Rationality

An appropriate and applicable norm here may be the following: participants in the market should have a reasonable opportunity to be well informed and should exercise freedom of choice rationally in their own interests (except when private advantage obviously conflicts with social welfare).[56]

Rationality is a meaningful idea because not all choice is simply a matter of taste. Some selections are made in order to achieve something else. In these cases, appraisal is a matter of scientific evaluation of how well the chosen means serve the given ends. When the evaluation is adverse, several explanations may be offered — ignorance, incompetence, lack of self-control, busyness, and indifference.[57]

Some of these explanations are used at times to justify denial of freedom of choice — for example, for juveniles, idiots and addicts, and with respect to insurance, medicine and funerals. In general, however, our culture instills in us a healthy respect for freedom of choice. We expect people to choose what they think is best for themselves, and the problem is viewed as one of providing them with an opportunity to avoid ignorance when making their selections.

An opportunity to avoid ignorance, however, is not subsumed in a call for free choice exercised rationally. Often no scientific evaluation is possible because matters of taste are involved.[58] Even in these cases factual information usually is relevant, and the only available criterion of wise choice is that participants have a reasonable opportunity to be well informed when making their selections.

This opportunity does not result automatically from the existence of freedom to advertise for participants on the other side of the market, even when the freedom is joined with a duty for them

---

states, making misleading advertising a misdemeanor. Very few states have adopted effective civil statutes pertaining to unfair competition. Federal legislation in general provides for a slap on the wrist. For a review of statutes applicable to interstate commerce, see C. Wilcox, Public Policies Toward Business, 2nd edition, Richard D. Irwin, Inc., Homewood, 1960, Chapter 8.

[56] As it does, for example, if needless surgery is prescribed.

[57] That people are incompetent or incapacitated does not imply that they will make irrational choices. All the alternatives presented to them may be reasonable selections. Thus, it is not necessary that 100 percent of buyers be shrewd in order to have a perfect rank correlation between quality and price. Ten percent could suffice to make a departure unprofitable to any seller. That a sufficient proportion is not always present is indicated by the numerous imperfect correlations reported by Consumers Research and Consumers Union.

[58] However, if people have conflicting preferences, such as before and after persuasive advertising, there is no intrusion implied in evaluating even a taste-related choice — evaluating it, for example, regarding health impact.

not to misrepresent. Even if all advertising that occurs in a market is socially desirable, it is unlikely that all will occur that would be desirable. Some information can increase sales in too many places to make its dissemination profitable to individual firms. Trade association activities may close the gap here, provided effective group action is undertaken. But dissemination of other information is not profitable even on a group basis — notably unfavorable and comparative information.

Provision of unfavorable information is likely to require imposition of affirmative duties of disclosure.[59] Providing patrons with a reasonable opportunity to make comparisons is likely to require the existence of mandatory coordination and impartial sources of information. Involved here are inspection, grading, standards of identity, standardized containers and packing, standardized quotations (including price per unit), price posting, market news and product tests.

A market may be regarded as deficient if any such measure would have greater benefits than costs and has not been instituted, or if irrational choices are being made for other reasons, or if freedom of choice has been unjustifiably denied.

Sometimes the deficiency can even be quantified: "The social costs of such irrational buying can be measured in terms of the difference between the farmers' total outlays on mixed fertilizer and what they would have been had farmers bought the same plant nutrients in the cheapest grades available."[60]

Conservation

According to Bain:

Conservation requires a choice of technique of exploitation, time pattern of production, and time patterns of investments and other costs, which together yield an optimal [present value of] net social benefit .... This abstract ideal ... [is] next to impossible to apply fully in the evaluation of

---

[59] A duty truthfully to disclose certain essential facts has been imposed by statute for a number of commodities. In addition, silence is actionable if it was likely to and did result in either bodily harm or physical damage to property, and also if the defendant chose to speak or imply but failed to reveal enough to negate misleading representations. There remains, however, no general duty to disclose all significant information.

[60] J. W. Markham, The Fertilizer Industry, The Vanderbilt University Press, Nashville, 1958, p. 188. The answer for 1950 was $60 million, or 10 percent. (pp. 194-95)

The importance of incomplete information is also stressed in R. L. Clodius, D. F. Fienup, R. L. Kristjanson, and C. Burnett, Procurement Policies and Practices of a Selected Group of Dairy Processing Firms, Wisconsin Agricultural Experiment Station Research Bulletins 193, 199, and 211 (1956, 1957, 1959).

actual performance. Using the definition as a general guide, however, it is possible to identify certain types of gross departure... (1) exploitation by a technique that raises both present and future costs...[as in petroleum]; (2) unduly rapid...use...which...[impairs] future use... [as in lumbering and fisheries]; and (3) pinching on current costs...which ...raises future costs of use disproportionately, as in agriculture. (pp. 401-02)

Another goal, "which in many cases is the cost practical approximation to the social optimum," is advocated by Ciriacy-Wantrup:

A safe minimum standard of conservation. In the [renewable but exhaustible] resource class...[it] is achieved by avoiding the critical zone — that is, those physical conditions, brought about by human action, which would make it uneconomical to halt and reverse depletion....It must also be shown that no other practice...accomplishes the same result more economically. The economic rationale for adopting a safe minimum standard in physical terms is allowance for uncertainty...[and] is based on the proposition that the costs of maintaining it are small in relation to the possible losses which irreversibility of depletion might entail....The safe minimum standard is a conceptual relative of the min-max solution....[61]

Both Bain and Ciriacy-Wantrup appear to condemn exhaustion to a renewable resource (provided the area is not to be turned to incompatible higher-valued uses, as with clearing timber for farming). This conclusion seems appropriate, given any plausible discount rate, in view of the relatively small sacrifices that apparently are required in order to sustain yields.

It also seems appropriate to condemn, secondly, certain methods of extracting a nonrenewable resource — namely, methods that needlessly reduce yield (as with competitive exploitation of an oil pool). This result, of course, can also be categorized as production inefficiency, as can ineffective use of the extracted resource by its consumers.

Concerning over-rapid (but not obviously inefficient) depletion of a nonrenewable resource, both Bain and Ciriacy-Wantrup appear to withhold judgment. Such circumspection seems appropriate in view of the possibilities both for discovery of new deposits and for substitution of other inputs. A judgment presumably would be appropriate in the extreme case where the price of a nonrenewable resource sank below marginal cost. This unlikely case can, however, be treated at least as well in terms of a violation of the norm for level of output.

---

[61] S. V. Ciriacy-Wantrup, Resource Conservation, Economics and Policies, University of California Press, Berkeley, 1952, pp. 250, 253, 259, 261, 262; "Conservation and Resource Programming," Proceedings of the 1960 Meeting of the American Association for the Advancement of Science, p. 110.

To the condemnation of needless depletion and inefficient extraction, all that may need to be added concerns, thirdly, the actual efforts made to discover additional deposits and substitutes. Such efforts should not persistently be ineffectual (as they would be with continuing reliance on divining rods) or obstructed (as by deadlock over royalties).[62]

External Effects

Traditionally, one conclusion concerning external effects has been emphasized. It is that their existence in the production or consumption of a commodity implies that the socially best level of output of the commodity differs from that associated with marginal private cost equals price.[63] This emphasis followed from the focus of welfare and monopoly theory on a particular question — namely, socially desirable levels of output and their relation to seller and buyer concentration — joined with an assumption of unchanging techniques and institutions.

I have already indicated that I regard precise fulfillment of a norm for industry output as relatively unimportant (and formulation of a precise norm as infeasible), and that I regard techniques and institutions as something manipulable. Hence, my emphasis is not on the need to adjust output because there are external burdens and benefits. It is on the need to reduce inappropriate burdens and to increase appropriate benefits.

The simple case involves uncompensated burdens that participants in the market could avoid at relatively small cost (for example, by moving), but nevertheless impose on outsiders, or unremunerative benefits that participants could provide to outsiders at relatively small cost (for example, by disclosing an intention to move), but nevertheless do not.

Often, however, the alternatives are not simply a well-defined pair of possibilities, and the question is not merely whether or not to avoid an injury or whether or not to provide a service. Thus, fumes and flood control are not all-or-nothing choices; each can be altered continuously. In this case the question is whether

---

[62] Bain mentions four causes of needless depletion and inefficient extraction (pp. 402-3, 628): (1) Competitive exploitation of fugacious resources under the rule of capture and without legal limits and/or compulsory unitization, (2) excessive private time preference, (3) poverty, (4) unenlightened management. Perhaps one could add: (5) no allowance for the social risk of exhaustion and (6) uncompensated benefits (as to the landlord or to lower lying land).

[63] No difference arises, however, in the case of long-run perfectly competitive adjustment to factor prices that, to the industry as a whole, are nonconstant with respect to quantity purchased.

uncompensated burdens exist that participants could <u>reduce</u> at relatively small cost, or whether unremunerative benefits exist that participants could <u>increase</u> at relatively small cost.

In either case, however, a single criterion of "relatively small cost" may be applied. It contrasts a pair of alternatives (I and II) that represent either qualitative opposites or one element in a series of step-type small differences, and it incorporates distributional considerations: "[A] movement from I to II ... [is warranted provided] gainers can overcompensate losers (though it may also be true that losers can overcompensate gainers to remain at I) plus a more equal distribution of welfare in the II position." [64]

I do not mean that nonoccurrence of any change fulfilling this criterion marks a deficiency in the market. The relevant sums cannot be estimated accurately, and "small" discrepancies might cost more to eliminate than they are worth. What I mean is that market practices should not involve an obviously and grossly excessive amount of uncompensated injury, or an obviously and grossly insufficient amount of uncompensated benefit. [65]

Labor Relations

This subject may be approached with four norms that I will present with a minimum of explanation. Most aspects of the norms are so general or vague that the emotive words carry their own defense.

First, training and hiring should not be done inefficiently nor made available on terms that exclude underprivileged people. [66]

Second, employees should not suffer needless discomfort, indignity, insecurity, arbitrariness, favoritism, partisanship, immobility or exploitation.

Third, employers should not suffer theft, ill will, featherbedding or deliberate restriction of effort below the cultural norm.

Fourth, there should be no unfair labor practices, [67] no work

---

[64] E. J. Mishan, "Welfare Criteria for External Effects," <u>American Economic Review</u>, September 1961, p. 607.

[65] The remedies available include moral suasion, civil liability and conditional subsidies, and prohibitions and requirements.

[66] An example of apparent inefficiency is the mobilization of seasonal agricultural labor and the pairing of jobs with people. For possible alternatives to present procedures, see V. Fuller, "The Background and Problems of Temporary Farm Employment in California," Statement at the Hearing of the California Senate Fact Finding Committee on Labor and Social Welfare, November 17, 1959, ditto.

[67] This phrase has denotative meaning. See, for example, G. F. Bloom and H. R. Northrup, <u>Economics of Labor Relations</u>, 4th edition, Richard D. Irwin, Inc., Homewood, 1961, p. 835.

stoppages,[68] no above-three-percent-negotiated increases in above-national-average wage rates[69] and no corruption or tyranny in the labor unions.

STANLEY K. SEAVER
University of Connecticut

DISCUSSION

S OSNICK FOLLOWS the generally accepted practice of discussing the behavior of the enterprise economy in three parts: (1) market structure, (2) market conduct and (3) market performance. Sosnick says "In the second place, no one really intends to include in the performance category every market attribute that is a result of market adjustments. To do so would destroy the distinction between the performance of a market and its structure and conduct. Structure and conduct would be included in the category of performance because they too are results." This is precisely the reason performance should not be discussed in isolation from structure and conduct and vice versa.

We are ultimately interested in the performance of the enterprise economy. And performance, the final result of the behavior of business enterprises, affects the welfare of everyone, for how business performs influences levels of employment, quantity of goods produced, the distribution of income and the payments to the factors. Now, as scientists we are curious about the determinants of performance, and hence, curious about "market structure" and "market conduct." But being good scientists we also ought to be curious about the direction of dependency. Does anyone believe that market performance does not significantly influence the "structure" and "conduct" of an industry? As Adelman so aptly put it:

---

[68] Work stoppages could be forbidden without eliminating the ability of employers and employees (unions) to exert "legitimate" economic pressure or their motivation to negotiate successfully. The substitute is a pair of taxes that would become effective after either side filed a "demand for suspension" and an appropriate authority determined that a legitimate dispute existed.

[69] Private output per man-hour paid in the United States increased during 1947-1958 at an average rate of approximately three percent per year. (See Trends in Output per Man-hour in the Private Economy, 1909-1958, United States Bureau of Labor Statistics Bulletin No. 1249, 1959.) If this unexpected rate continues, an over-all rise in money wage rates as large as three percent per year is compatible with price stability even without wage-earners' share of national income increasing. Because the latter cannot be expected, or at least cannot be expected indefinitely, a deflated three percent is the suggested maximum raise where existing wage rates are not obviously low.

Yet it is impossible to study structure without knowing performance; specifically, one cannot do so elementary a task as to count the number of sellers in a market without first knowing something of the boundaries of the market; boundaries are defined by a gap in the chain of substitutes, or, more generally, the decline of substitution to the point where it may be safely neglected, and this can only be found by looking at price-cost behavior.[1]

Is there any doubt that the number of firms in an industry, classified as an attribute of structure, does not influence efficiency of the industry, an attribute of performance, which in turn must largely determine the method (collusive or otherwise) of arriving at common prices, an attribute of market conduct? Sosnick recognizes this when he says: "Virtually, every market attribute is influenced by other market attributes, and the chain of influence is circular and endless." Economists have tended to view "structure," "conduct," and "performance" as independent areas of research. Such a view ignores reality and is a guarantee of useless research results. No one should be under the illusion that performance is anything but complementary with "structure" and "conduct."

The term "market" has been defined in so many ways that it would seem appropriate to spend a moment to make explicit its meaning in the present context. Mason[2] seems to prefer that a market be defined with respect to the position of a single seller or buyer. But he quickly proceeds to define seller's market as one which includes all considerations which the seller takes into account, in determining his business policies. Hence the seller's market would include all buyers and sellers, whose actions he considers as influencing his sales or purchases. A market then must include, as Bain says, "all the sellers in an individual industry, and all the buyers to whom (in common) they sell." This still leaves some doubts as to the extent of the market and presumably this is why Joan Robinson suggested the bounds of an industry be delineated by a gap in the chain of substitutes. In modern terms, then, a market would be a group of sellers and buyers in an industry producing such close substitutes as to render the price cross-elasticities of demand extremely high. Hence, an industry and a market are one and the same.

Now for some comments on five of Sosnick's twelve issues — namely, production efficiency, technological progressiveness, profit rates, level of output and costs of sales promotion, for which some operational norms are desired.

[1] M. A. Adelman "Economic Concepts of Competition," Journal of Farm Economics, Vol. 41, No. 5, December 1959, pp. 1198.
[2] E. S. Mason, Economic Concentration and the Monopoly Problems, Harvard University Press, Cambridge, 1957, p. 65.

PRODUCTION EFFICIENCY

I agree with most, if not all, of the listed dangers and difficulties in providing an adequate norm for evaluating efficiency. I do not, however, understand the statement "The point is that an operational norm will not refer to minimum costs. It will specify merely that no real costs persist that are clearly unnecessary to provide the use values that are being provided." But to abandon minimum costs means to abandon any norm. We would simply be substituting a statement which said costs are what they are and generally above minimum costs. How does one know "that no real costs persist that are clearly unnecessary to provide the use values that are being provided" unless one is able to make some statement about what real costs could be, given some other organization of resources. And another organization of resources may produce minimum costs.

The long-run unit cost curve refers to the scale (size) effect on unit cost under the assumption that plants of differing scale will be constantly and continuously operated at that rate of output, per hour and per year, for which they were designed. And certainly scale of plant means the particular rate of output at which that plant or firm gives a lower cost than any other scale. In actual practice no individual plant can operate very long at a constant rate of output. Consequently, each plant or firm will be operating at some rate of output generally below the optimum or best rate previously indicated, which implies the plant will generally not be operating at minimum cost.

Given all the factors which the firms take into account (including an "engineering error"), it should be possible to determine a long-run average unit cost at which a plant or firm actually operates for each alternative scale. And this must be similar to what E. A. G. Robinson[3] was referring to in any actual case of scale-cost relations; namely, we must mean a firm which, given the existing conditions of technique and organizing ability, has the lowest average cost of production per unit when all costs which must be covered in the long run are included.

It should be possible to calculate a ratio between minimum cost for alternative sizes of plants or firms and the lowest average cost referred to by Robinson which could include many of the niceties suggested by Sosnick. Such a ratio would generally be above one. What needs to be argued by the profession is the limit of an acceptable ratio, with allowances being made for variations between industries. If agreement can be reached, we would have an acceptable norm.

[3] E. A. G. Robinson, The Structure of Competitive Industry, University of Chicago Press, Chicago, 1962, p. 11.

There are, of course, some disconcerting matters about using such a ratio as an approximation of a "true" efficiency norm. For example, assume that the ratio obtained was two. Does this mean that the plant is inefficient? Such a ratio might result from the firm's having built facilities larger than the most efficient for present output but having done so in anticipation of expanding future output and its expectations for securing monopoly gains which would outweigh high present per-unit costs.

Another disturbing factor is that firms must adjust to fluctuating output in their attempts to achieve minimum average cost as defined. However, a firm which is optimum under conditions of constant output — the assumption of minimum costs of scale — is probably not optimum under conditions of fluctuating output. In other words, it is probably cheaper to manufacture a small quantity of ball bearings in a small plant than in an underemployed large plant.

Also disturbing is the cherished idea of economists that the survival of the lowest cost is the fittest. The merits of this idea leave me somewhat uneasy about accepting any firm's cost as the basis of a norm for measuring efficiency. My uneasiness stems from two likely adjustments faced by firms in an industry experiencing a cost-price "squeeze."

One, a firm with high costs is generally the first to experience difficulties and thus the first to receive financial assistance. Remaining lower-cost firms eventually run into trouble, appeal for financial assistance, are refused because of lack of confidence in the industry or lack of loanable funds. Billie Sol Estes was correct in his belief that the size of the debt is related to the creditors' interest in survival, when he said: "If you get into somebody far enough, you've got yourself a partner."

Two, many of the lowest-cost and best-adapted firms exit of their own accord during industry depressions. The Connecticut broiler industry does not today include all the most efficient producers of five years ago.

Finally, efficiency can only be discussed relative to given market conditions facing the firm or plant. The firms must not only be technologically efficient, but efficient at predicting future demand. Since the demand curves facing the individual firms are not identical, there exists the possibility of more than one size of plant or firm with minimum average costs of production for a given output. What is the prescription under such circumstances? I do not know.

But developing an efficiency norm becomes a simple mathematical problem when compared to specifying usable and accurate criteria for handling progressiveness. The difficulty arises largely because of the inadequacy of capital theory — perhaps the inadequacy of economists — in explaining the generation of technology. Despite this, let me compliment Sosnick for the manner in which he discusses the issue. Technology has long been glossed over by economists and is much more important in determining the performance of a market (industry) than most other attributes.

TECHNOLOGICAL PROGRESSIVENESS

But what measures can be applied which will tend to evaluate the performance of an industry in adopting new technology over time? I should like to propose one — output per man-hour — in addition to those discussed by Sosnick. Fellner[4] has called attention to at least two limitations to man-hour output is being a precise measure of "progressiveness": (1) Movements along a given production function may lead to changes in man-hour output; and (2) improvements quite obviously do not express themselves alone in man-hour output. Output per man-hour has not increased smoothly at all times, but has shown long-time increases of from 2 to 3 compound percent per year. This undoubtedly varies considerably by industries; therefore, some bench marks of acceptable rates in various industries need to be established. But where output per man-hour in any industry is not showing rather continuous improvement, the industry must be performing "badly." And, says Fellner, "the significance of the phenomena [increasing output per man-hour] outweighs the importance of a great many that can be observed on a static level of analysis."

Regarding profit rates, I have never realized until now I should be so concerned with losses. This probably reflects the malallocation of my energies in the direction of concern with excess profits. But Sosnick puts rather succinctly all he or anyone else needs to say about losses when he says: "In a word, the losses should be 'moderate.'" I fail to see any necessary additions.

PROFIT RATES

But now comes the stickler, which occupies the largest portion (and rightly so) of the chapter. Sosnick raises the following questions:

---

[4] William Fellner, Competition Among the Few, Alfred A. Knopf, New York, 1949, p. 285.

1. What magnitude represents an unusual rate of return,
    when consideration is given to extenuating circum-
    stances as determinants of high or unjustifiable profits?

2. How long-lived a return do the circumstances justify?

3. Granting that unjustifiable profits can be identified,
    does it follow that they should be condemned?

Something less than a positive answer to any of the three questions is indicated by Sosnick's closing remark to this section.
"The observer should not be so distracted by profit rates that he
neglects the important aspects of performance." What might one
consider "a more important aspect"?

It is one thing to arrive at informed judgments about the profit
attribute of performance and quite a different matter to develop
some empirical test. Yet, the logic of being able to detect persistent departures from competitive behavior by a study of price-
cost and profit data seems so strong that I hate to admit we have
nothing positive to say about the level of profits. To say nothing
leaves us in the position Sosnick seems to justify; that is, identifying the sources of the excessive profit somehow makes it less
excessive. We are asked to accept justifications for positive
profits, e.g., socially useful innovation and unusually favorable
cost performance, simply because no plausible or reasonably precise standards are available for evaluation.

Plants cannot operate at full capacity or at minimum cost defined as marginal cost equal to average cost equal to price — the
requirements of perfect competition. We are dealing with demand
curves, something less than perfectly horizontal, facing the firms.
What is required is a demand curve with sufficient slope to bring
price on the average far enough above marginal cost so that average cost may be covered over good and bad times. As mentioned
earlier, this is why efficiency cannot be discussed without reference to the demand facing the firm. And the firm must exercise
enough price flexibility to stimulate demand in recessions and the
reverse during expansion. (Flexibility aspects of market performance have been ignored.) So price is expected to be above short-
run marginal cost, and by enough to cover average cost over time.

Let's look at it another way. If costs are carefully defined as
the market value of all factors including management, labor, capital and including imputed costs, then we should be able to say
something positive about profits. (And, incidentally, technological innovations as generated in modern laboratories are already
part of the present cost of doing business and do not need to be
allocated to profit tomorrow to cover all costs of technological

development.) But costs are not defined as including the market value of any special barriers to entry of other sellers, whether these be advertising, patent purchase but not use, capital withholdings directly or indirectly and many others.

This is one of the reasons why entry becomes such an important issue in performance. Further, Sosnick includes numerous extenuating circumstances in his definition of costs, including provision for anticipation of short-run losses. If all extenuating circumstances are included in cost, then our problem becomes one of determining the amount it is "reasonable" to allocate to cover such circumstances. Furthermore, prices above costs defined as including everything are excessive and no further justification or explanation seems necessary. If this is what Sosnick means by "... except that such accompanied profits are undesirable if they both exceed a justifiable level (if such can be determined) and contribute to inequality. (6) Profits not so accompanied are undesirable if they contribute to inequality or to perpetuation of excess capacity; ... " then we are in agreement.

Incidentally, the measurement of excessive profits is often very simple. There is a surprising number of instances where individuals and firms admit, at least privately, to profits so high as to be embarrassing. This might be suggested as a norm which is unencumbered with definitional, moral, ethical or other problems.

I agree with Sosnick that the income distribution effects of unjustifiable profits do not seem so disturbing, but I am greatly concerned about the impact of excess profits on allocation of resources. Industries with high excess profits must be restricting output and thereby are denying millions of consumers an opportunity to maximize satisfaction.

One possibility for measuring profits should be emphasized. Why not simply compare the level of profits in two industries, each being faced with approximately the same costs, technological developments and capital requirements? Profits in one industry consistently and considerably higher than those in the other should indicate the desirable direction resources should move. The foregoing is only a relative measure and would not be a test of the possible "unjustifiable" absolute level in both industries. But the relative level is the essential measure for directing resources.

There are, however, some indefinite aspects to any quantitative measure of profits which is to be used as a norm. High profits persisting over a long period of time in an industry not growing rapidly is indicative of underinvestment. Assuming the terms "growing rapidly" and "long period of time" can be defined, a rather specific measure of market performance would be available. But it is quite possible, given a constant and fairly rapid shift to the right in the demand curve facing an industry, that excess profits can persist for reasonably long periods of time. And given continued growth (continued adoption of technology, and growth in investment and output per man-hour) the industry still may show high profits. Under such circumstances, high profits would not necessarily mean the industry was performing badly, unless one defines poor prediction as bad performance.

LEVEL OF OUTPUT

I should like to make a brief comment on the fourth issue, namely, level of output. I am somewhat unclear about the assumption underlying proposition three which says "that output is insufficient if it would be greater at lower prices and if the ratios of price to short-run marginal (social) cost regularly are greater than in identifiable competing industries." Competitive equilibrium specifies that the ratio between marginal private cost in any two industries be equal to the ratio of the prices of the products being considered. However, if our industry is characterized by large divergence between marginal social cost and marginal private cost, then the ratio between marginal social cost in our industry and in the other industry will not be equal to the ratio between prices. In any instances where private costs are in excess of social cost it will be socially profitable and privately unprofitable to make a shift.

The reverse also obtains. For output to be optimum under perfect competition it is necessary to assume that no divergence between marginal private and social cost of an increase in output is in fact possible. Some best output can still be obtained if the divergence between marginal private and social cost is approximately the same in the two or several industries under consideration. The dilemma is that on the American economic scene the ratio of marginal private and social cost is unlikely to be approximately equal as between industries.

I agree with Sosnick that his seven propositions leave a large gap, to wit: Prices exceed short-run and long-run marginal social costs; marginal costs are positive; lower prices are not apt to increase profits and ratios of prices to marginal costs in competing industries are difficult to measure. (I do not agree when he says they cannot be measured.) He does not know how to close this gap and neither do I, but this does not lead me to Sosnick's conclusion that filling the gap is not a serious omission. And I am not impressed with citing the Harberger study as evidence that the aggregate welfare loss associated with misallocation in the manufacturing sector is really very small after all.

SALES PROMOTION

Finally, the discussion of sales promotion shows a careful and considered analysis of a highly emotional issue. It states very succinctly the possibilities of establishing objective criteria of performance for this attribute. But allow me an emotional outburst in the form of two questions. Would it be possible to permit advertising only on the basis of the degree of product homogeneity in the industry? Where the industry is characterized by a substantial degree of homogeneity (steel, aluminum, cigarette and probably large segments of the food industry — generally the producer-goods industries), no advertising would be allowed. Excellent TV programs might be missed — but what a pleasure to forego hearing "Winston tastes good like a cigarette should." Where the product of competing sellers was "moderately" homogenous (gasoline), advertising would only be permitted when a new product was introduced. Where a high degree of heterogeneity exists Sosnick's general principles could be invoked. The degree of homogeneity in each instance could be determined by price cross elasticity of demand.

The second question is: Would it be possible to allow advertising as a cost of doing business (to permit determination of excess profit) but not allow it as an income tax exemption? My boiling point is extremely low when subjected to misleading, deceptive and downright false advertising while simultaneously realizing the amount of tax dollars society is foregoing. These two questions leave my bias showing, but I believe they can be economically and socially defended.

The timid probably long ago have retired to their Marshallian stronghold to restore faith in themselves and their intellectual abilities. The somewhat more bold will probably again embrace monopolistic and imperfect competition theories in hopes of yet remaining virginal. And if their retreat has been due to their inability to find valid generalizations about criteria which will permit the quantification of important variables affecting market performance, the retreat is probably justified. But if Marshallian and imperfect competition theories have made neat and tidy undergraduate classroom presentation, they have left something to be desired in terms of operational applicability, and I applaud all attempts to find more workable and acceptable means of proceeding.

I do not believe Sosnick's careful cataloging of numerous issues to be considered and resolved is meant to frighten us into doing nothing, simply because all the criteria are not intuitively obvious. Further it is not necessary to consider all twelve of the issues raised in order to do acceptable professional work in market performance. Yntema has suggested that what concerns us most in market performance is a distinction between five percent and fifty percent "causes." My suggestion is that we concentrate on (1) productive efficiency; (2) technological progressiveness; (3) profit rates; (4) level of output and (5) cost of sales promotion.

WILLARD F. MUELLER
Federal Trade Commission

DISCUSSION

SOSNICK HAS DONE an excellent job of reviewing the literature of his subject, and has demonstrated well the difficult problems confronting those courageous enough to concern themselves with the normative aspects of industrial performance. Of late, too many economists have shied away from the great normative problems of our day and have busied themselves instead with esoteric refinements of economic theory and sterile applications.

Sosnick begins by defining and clarifying the concept of market performance. This and subsequent discussion demonstrate the great debt we owe to Bain for his efforts to classify and define the various concepts pertinent to the study of industrial organization. For while we may not always agree with Bain in particulars, his work has become the natural starting point for subsequent discussions. Sosnick feels that Bain's definition of market performance needs clarification; Sosnick would define market performance as "the attributes of production and exchange in a segment of the economy that directly influence the welfare of the participants and the society. These attributes represent some, but not all, of the results of participants' adjustments to expected demand and supply opportunities in the market, and of adjustments to other things too." (p. 85)

Although I cannot disagree with this definition of market performance, neither do I find it inconsistent with Bain's definition.

Sosnick turns next to the dimensions of market performance,

*These comments reflect the views of the author and not necessarily those of the Federal Trade Commission.

and adds others to those suggested by Bain. He then turns to the main purpose of his chapter, which is to discuss "dimension norms for performance." The subsequent treatment is lengthy and somewhat discouraging. With only few exceptions the norms never reach the adequacy test he prescribed at the outset. As he put it, "The norm will be operational if it implies a set of feasible actions that will, for an actual market situation, produce a dichotomous rating (such as 'workable' or 'unworkable') — or better, a quantification of actual versus optimum performance in the dimension and issue."

PROFIT RATES AND PERFORMANCE

I will discuss two points, one dealing with what I think is an error in Sosnick's discussion, and, second, with an omission. I think Sosnick goes too far in dismissing profit rates of firms as an indicator of market performance. He feels that persistently high profits are not meaningful indicators of a misallocation of resources or an inequitable distribution of income. With this I cannot agree. First, the study he cites (p. 40) by Harberger to support the contention that no serious misallocation results from monopoly has been demonstrated to be riddled with erroneous assumptions and inadequate data. Second, high profits made possible by market power may be only the visible cap of the misallocation iceberg. The submerged portion may include abnormally high salaries for entrenched management and abnormally high wages for labor. The steel industry may be a leading example of the latter situation. Certainly few would deny that big steel's potential ability to protect or enhance its profits by passing on wage increases to consumers through increased prices has served as a tantalizing attraction to organized labor's demands for higher wages. The end result of this particular situation has been to permit steel price increases which are far out of line with price increases in the rest of the economy. One result has been to make this important industry less competitive in the world market, which, in turn, has contributed to the deterioration in our balance of payments. Certainly this is misallocation of resources on a large scale.

Gardiner Means asserts that high profits also discourage desirable social performance for the following reason:

"...the public interest is damaged by the use of pricing power to create too high a rate of return on capital — the failure to invest new capital in improved techniques or products as rapidly as would be economical. If a

corporation has to see an average probability of making 16 percent on a
new and more efficient machine or a new product, it will be less progressive than if it only requires an average probability of 8 percent. And if
capital is available at the latter figure, growth is less rapid than would be
economical."[1]

The point I am making is that persistently excessive profits
made possible by positions of entrenched market power may result in considerably greater misallocations of resources than at
first meets the eye. Moreover, persistently high profits are a
significant indicator of performance because their existence indicates the presence of entrenched market power, which may be
undesirable for other reasons than those discussed above. These
may be noneconomic as well as economic in nature.

PUBLIC POLICY

Finally, a word about the usefulness for public policy of the
performance norms specified in this chapter. Pragmatism might
seem to argue for a public policy toward competitive conduct
which would consider the twelve — and perhaps more — performance norms specified by Sosnick when evaluating, say, the probable impact of a merger on future performance. Economists of
the performance school of workable competition have urged just
such an approach in antitrust enforcement. However, careful
study of Sosnick's discussion of these norms reveals why such an
approach is precisely the least pragmatic approach possible. A
careful reading of Sosnick's chapter indicates that economists
have precious little which they can say with precision about the
relationship between most performance norms and their causes.
Consequently, a public policy which would rely on economic
measurement of numerous performance attributes of alternative
courses of action turns out to be completely unworkable.

The British experience with pragmatic antitrust enforcement
illustrates this point vividly. The Economist, in an article discussing the contemplated merger of England's two greatest chemical complexes, made some refreshing observations of the differences between the British and American approach toward
antitrust matters. It said, in part:

The Government's commitment to empiricism in examining monopoly
and restrictive practices would in any case have given it excuses for de-

---

[1] G. C. Means, Pricing Power and the Public Interest, Harper & Brothers, New
York, 1962, p. 159.

ciding... not to decide whether this merger would or would not be in the national interest. Such empiricism — monopoly's not good or bad, but thinking (by the Monopolies Commission afterwards) makes it so — is built into British political attitudes towards the restraint of competition....
The Government's entranced indecision before the prospect of ICI's gobbling up Courtaulds is only the latest demonstration of the basic inadequacy of this whole political attitude, which sounds so sensible and constantly turns out to be so ineffectual.

It arises perhaps from the mistaken assumption — which economists are guilty of encouraging — that political objections to monopoly can be altogether based on evidential grounds, economic or technical. The United States — which is often accused in Europe of having an exaggerated animus against monopoly, because it has a policy that quite often works — seldom falls into this trap. Its legal prejudice, per se, against anything calculated to restrain competition, is avowedly based, in the last resort, on social and even moral grounds; the economic efficiency that it believes competition generally promotes is the secondary justification, not the first. Primarily, American attitudes towards monopoly (public as well as private) are based upon a distrust of concentrations of economic power, irresponsible in that they are not finally accountable to the public. This does not make American antitrust legislation emotional and ineffective: it makes it at times even embarrassingly effective.[2]

Although economists have contributed much toward the development and enforcement of our antitrust laws, it is fortunate indeed that the development and enforcement of these laws did not await conclusive empirical verification of the relevant relationship between market structure and market performance.

---

[2]"No Policy for Mergers," The Economist, February 3, 1962, pp. 393-94.

PART FOUR

WORKSHOP CONCLUSIONS

Chapter 7

REPORT OF WORKGROUP 1
Vernon Sorenson, Chairman
Michigan State University

Relation between managerial goals and values and market behavior and structure

W E CONCEIVED OUR PURPOSE in the broadest sense to be that of attempting to shed some light on the role and nature of managerial activity and its implications for firm behavior and market results, including structural adjustment in agricultural markets. Our interests in understanding managerial activity follows from at least two general kinds of considerations: (1) We would like to be able to explain and understand why firms behave as they do in agricultural markets to improve our ability to predict their response to changing situations and (2) we want to know how management should function to obtain a given set of results.

At first blush the problem of looking at firm behavior and the managerial process appears to be unmanageably complex. This reflects the many dimensions that represent the environment within which firms operate and the multiplicity of factors that must be taken into account when business decisions are made. We can gain some perspective if as a first step we develop a classification of the relevant variables involved.

VARIABLES IN FIRM BEHAVIOR

Three classes of variables are relevant in looking at firm behavior. These are: outcomes, behavioral variables and a set of variables that specifies the internal and external conditions that face the firm. These classes of variables can be presented schematically as shown in Figure 7.1.

Reading from right to left, Figure 7.1 suggests that firms will act to attain certain kinds of results or outcomes. These arise

138

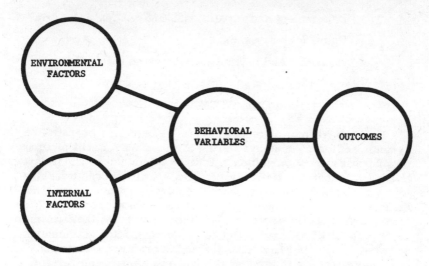

Figure 7.1. Classification of variables in a model of firm behavior.

when firms make decisions and take actions related to pricing, production, promotion and organization. The behavioral variables (pricing, etc.) can be manipulated by the firm to attain sought-after ends or goals. The kinds of action taken and the results of the action will be influenced in turn by conditions internal to the firm and conditions external to the firm. The outcomes that the firm attains will include its rate of earnings or profit levels, cost levels, market penetration, market power and organizational adjustment.

The conditions or situations that influence behavior and outcomes will vary widely in content and in importance between firms and industries. This presents a problem of developing an adequate classification with sufficient detail to fit all circumstances. We would suggest, however, that the following general classifications are relevant in most situations.

A. Variables internal to the firm

   1. The firm's physical and human resource base including managerial resources.

   2. The firm's physical and administrative organization.

   3. The goals or objectives of the firm.

B. Environmental factors

   1. Physical and technological environment

2. Government and institutional environment

3. Cultural environment

4. Economic and market environment

THE ROLE OF MANAGEMENT

The need for management arises because firms operate in a dynamic setting. The above listing provides only a still picture or snapshot view of variables relevant to firm behavior. It serves to illustrate that an extremely complex set of interrelationships in the general environment, market environment and internal to the firm specify the range of alternatives open to the firm. These factors influence the decisions and actions taken by the firm in an attempt to fulfill its goals. But these decisions and actions must be taken in a world where changes and interaction are continuing phenomena that occur in many dimensions. Any of the variables in the firm's environment may change at any time and at different rates. The state of the arts and sciences may change through invention and innovation. Consumer tastes and preferences may change, new firms may enter the market, public policy may change, etc. Because environment is constantly changing, plans must be formulated with imperfect knowledge of the future. As a result, errors will occur and plans often will not be fulfilled as expected.

A further source of change is that which is created by the actions of the firm itself. Firms take actions to change consumer taste and preferences through advertising and promotion programs. Lobbying is aimed at changing the governmental environment. Other actions may change the internal conditions of the firm. Actions that result in profits or losses will change the resource base from which the firm operates and, as suggested by Penrose,[1] the process of solving problems and engaging in managerial activity inherently changes the quality of the managerial resource and provides a better basis for solving future problems and arriving at decisions and actions.

Because change is continuous there is a continuing need for adjustment in the firm's status and its relationship to its environment. This continuous change plus the fact of limitations on man's perceptual ability leads to imperfect knowledge and foresight. Lack of perfect knowledge and foresight leads in turn to

---

[1] Edith Penrose, The Theory of the Growth of the Firm, John Wiley & Sons, Inc., New York, 1959.

the need for the functions of management to be carried out on a continuous basis. In this context management faces a number of responsibilities. It must:

A. Formulate goals

B. Perceive problems and opportunities

C. Gather information

D. Analyze information

E. Make decisions

F. Initiate and administer action

G. Assume responsibility

H. Evaluate actions taken

If we attribute these roles to management, then it seems pertinent to ask ourselves how management is organized to do the job, how individual managerial processes are performed and how they relate to the behavior of the firm.

As a starting point for enumerating problems related to research on management and firm behavior, we suggest the following list of items for consideration with the thought that each represents a researchable area that can improve our ability to comprehend dynamic processes in agricultural markets.

A. Gathering and Analyzing Information

One of the functions of management (or as might be conceived inputs into decision making) is the role of information — its collection, analysis and use. In attacking this management function we might conceive of the following separate issues:

1. How direction is given to the information-seeking activity; the connection between problem perception of management and the information-gathering process

2. Organizations and resources established for acquiring information

3. Sources of information used (these could be viewed as from three sources):
   (a) Internally generated from the firm's operations
   (b) Available from joint efforts of the firm with the organizations
   (c) Publicly available

4. Methods used in analyzing the data

5. What is done with the analyzed data

Variation in the above informational issues could be hypothesized as having a causal effect on: (a) relative rates of growth,
(b) innovation and progressiveness, (c) profit rates, (d) rates of
entry and exit into an industry.

Variables which might be causal in these differences in the
operation and performance of this particular managerial function
might be: Type of firm ownership; size of firm; philosophy and
background of management; product mix of the firm; size and
dynamics of the external market.

B. Goal Formulation

Does management explicitly formulate goals for the firm and
if so, how? How does management weigh basic concepts of good
or bad and factual concepts about the firm's internal conditions
and its environment in arriving at a set of goals or objectives?
In judging a firm's operations it certainly becomes necessary to
have some idea of the goals that a firm has in its operations. Although the study and analysis of goals are recognized as being
very difficult methodologically, such difficulty should not preclude effort in answering the problem. Also, if analysis of other
factors of management keeps this issue of goal variations in
mind, substantial progress in knowledge in this area may come
as a by-product.

C. The Nature of the Managerial Resource

What does the management resource consist of and can managerial ability be identified? How are managerial resources organized within the firm and what decisions are delegated to various
administrative levels? Can qualitative factors, such as the nature
of individual response to risk and uncertainty, level of motivation
and ability to perceive problems and respond to opportunities be
recognized?

D. Development of Strategies

How do firms develop appropriate strategies for dealing with
uncertainty and unexpected outcomes? Under what circumstances

do they build in flexibility: diversify, integrate, hedge, buy insurance, seek market power or otherwise adjust operations to
overcome uncertainty?

E. Administrative Processes

How do firms organize to implement action and administer
decisions that have been made by management? How do appropriate organization and the skills needed vary under different
circumstances? What communication processes are established?

F. Behavior of Firms

With some understanding of the nature of managerial inputs
and processes the basis should be available for establishing more
meaningful hypotheses concerning how firms arrive at decisions
on pricing, production, promotion, research and innovation, firm
growth and organizational adjustment; how these will vary under
different circumstances; and how firms will adjust their position
in response to changes in internal or environmental conditions.

Can specific problem areas be isolated and evaluated? The
process of firm growth, for example, may involve vertical integration, diversification and horizontal growth or product line expansion. No existing theoretical framework provides a fully
satisfactory basis for developing hypotheses or analytical models
for analyzing firm growth behavior. The same probably is true
for other behavioral variables. For example, it is unlikely that
promotion behavior of the firm is motivated entirely by a desire
to differentiate a product, nor is pricing based solely on profit
maximization.

Approaching these problems in a management framework
raises questions of analytical methods. First we need to ask how
we define the firm for analysis of managerial behavior. In the
market structure context the firm is defined as a unit of productive resources that may not be synonymous with the decision-
making unit. This becomes a major issue of measuring entry and
exit as well as market structures and the relationship between
managerial and physical inputs. These and numerous other
methodological questions undoubtedly will arise.

SUMMARY

The kinds of insights suggested by the above six problem areas
are needed to evaluate market performance for policy purposes
and to develop educational and service activities needed to improve market performance. It will not, however, be easy to attain
them. Initially, the study of business decision making and firm
behavior must draw on a number of distinct fields of learning in
order to develop appropriate hypotheses and to formulate logical
and testable analytical models that produce meaningful results.

In line with the theme of this volume we might ask if research
on management will provide the basis wherein market structure
analysis can become a dynamic instead of a static approach to examining existing conditions. Obviously this is a major issue that
is embedded in performance variables, such as rate of "growth"
and rate of technological innovations. The study of management
as a variable may furnish a key in this problem since it can be a
study of the paths and movement of firms and of how decisions are
made to take various kinds of actions.

Chapter 8

REPORT OF WORKGROUP 2
G. G. Judge
and
George Brinegar, Chairmen
University of Illinois

Analytic and quantitative techniques and data needs for measurement in market structure research

O UR OBJECTIVE is to explore analytical techniques for measurement and data needs in market structure research. If this purpose is to be sought with any success, attention must first be directed toward asking why market structure research is worth doing or more specifically "measurement for what." If this question is answered then (perhaps) the analytical framework(s) under which the research analyses are to proceed can be delineated and more efficient choices can be made among analytical and quantitative techniques and the measurement of what.

MEASUREMENT FOR WHAT

"Measurement for what" in the context of market structure research has many reasonable and appropriate answers in terms of final objectives. We assume that the interest of agricultural economists with structure or competition is primarily an interest with a maximizing orientation; i.e., what effect does the organization of an industry have upon pricing and, indirectly, resource use and welfare and the distribution of income. Within this framework market structure research may be conducted to focus upon such problems as (1) the efficiency of the enterprise system in price determination, resource allocation, in rationing goods and services, in setting relative values in accord with the notion of consumer sovereignty, in distributing income and promoting economic growth; (2) maximizing and minimizing problems significant to individual firms and groups of firms and (3) the concentration and diffusion of economic and political power.

145

A STRATEGY FOR RESEARCH

Such a vast array of final objectives for market structure research is likely to seduce the researcher into the collection of
great masses of data and attendant descriptive efforts unless
some method of placing limits on what is relevant is specified.
We suggest the following: Since we are ultimately interested in
the performance of the enterprise economy and desire to know how
this performance can be improved, both in the short and long run
in relation to a firm, a group of firms or an industry, perhaps the
place to start the research is not to look for relationships between market structure and performance, but rather to concentrate on ascertaining the firm, group of firms or industries where
outcomes leave the most to be desired — i.e., have the greatest
impact on reducing total welfare. Then knowing the major problem industry or industries, research efforts could then be directed
to ascertaining where significant performance gaps exist, why
these industries are performing badly or what generates the performance gap and how this poor performance may be mitigated.

In other words, we view the search for knowledge in regard to
industry performance as a sequential process. First by means
of rough tests or general indicators the trouble spot industries
are located and ranked for research purposes. The industry or
industries chosen are then studied in great depth and detail and
the gaps between desired and actual performance are made explicit. Why these gaps obtain are then investigated and alternative recommendations and prescriptions for closing these gaps
may be suggested.

It should be noted that this approach does not follow the usual
methodology employed in market structure investigations, since
it does not emphasize research directed toward establishing
unique functional relationships between market structure attributes and performance. This omission of studying structure per
se is based on the beliefs that (1) causality flows both ways, (2)
only rarely can general inferences about performance be drawn
from a knowledge of structure, (i.e., many factors can cause an
industry to perform badly and structure is only one of the generating forces) and (3) that information of the structure performance
variety is useful in only two contexts; when a part of an intensive
study or as a "rough" indication of likely problem areas.

Quantitative Methods and the Measurement of What

Within the above framework we suggest the following procedures:

1. In order to locate the industry or industries that generate welfare losses and to get a rough idea of a priority ranking that may be used for research purposes, the following strategies may be employed.

   a. As a first rough approximation, partition the agricultural sector into meaningful industries. Given this classification, set up a rough input-output tableau which will show the interdependence of the industries. The idea here is that the performance of one industry necessarily affects the performance of other industries if they are interrelated. Therefore, a rough tableau of the input-output variety will indicate the interrelations between industries in the agricultural sector and suggest which industries have the greatest degree of interdependence and thus would have a chance to affect the performance that other industries could obtain. An industry with a high degree of interdependence would then be a candidate for further investigation.

   b. The second test that might be employed to decide the direction of research resources would be to use general indicators that provide a rough test of the presence or absence of problem firms or industries. These crude results would then indicate specific situations worth further investigation. As a guide for arriving at these general indicators or rough tests we recommend that they be tied back to the more general problem areas, such as price determination and reflection, resource allocation, income distribution, growth, etc.; i.e., given these broad problem areas rough tests would be generated for determining imperfections. For example, for price determination and reflection one might use such rough measures as (1) price rigidities over time, (2) inadequate variation in prices over space, (3) price $\gtrless$ marginal cost, (4) profit margin, (5) freight absorption practices and (6) dumping. Similar rough measures could be provided for the other major economic problem areas. These rough measures will, on occasion, be those structural characteristics normally listed or emphasized by market structure researchers.

   With the aid of these crude tests problems of specific industries may be so serious that no further identification research is needed. It may be that immediate solutions — not necessarily the long-run optimum solutions — can be suggested and certain lines of action are clear. In such cases prescriptions or recommendations may be developed with little if any additional research on the basis of past experience or even common sense, although as many people have made mistakes using common-sense approaches as by the failure to use common sense. Oftentimes, however, the problem areas that are approximately located with the general indicators will require much additional research. This then leads to the next step in the research process.

2. Using the rough tests or general indicators to locate a major potential problem area or areas the firm, group of firms or industry will then be investigated in great detail. Information will be obtained both spatially and over time on such things as factor and product prices, level of outputs and inputs, factor and product flows, cost functions for the operating plants and firms, etc. This information will thus specify the situation as it has existed over time for the industry in question, i.e., the "where we are and have been aspects."

Given this information, interest would then shift to what could obtain under present conditions. As a vehicle or framework for this research interregional economic activity analysis equilibrium models could be employed. The competitive (efficiency) model could be used as a criterion for generating the "could be" results.

In general terms the analysis may proceed as follows: Let the economy be divided into regions. For the agricultural sector, commodities are partitioned into resources or primary commodities which are not desired in themselves (these resources may be either mobile or immobile); intermediate commodities which are produced commodities emerging from a production process as an output and not desired in themselves; and final commodities which are produced commodities desirable in themselves.

Technial data needed for the analysis are regional demand relations for the final products, technical input-output data for the plants or firms, regional plant capacities, regional resource endowments and other sector demands for the resources and intermediate commodities and transportation rates for the primary, intermediate and final commodities.

Given these data, an interregional activity analysis model could be estimated which would yield regional prices for the final, intermediate and primary (mobile) commodities and rents for the immobile primary commodities, the regional level of output for each final and intermediate commodity, the regional level of resource use and the level of interregional flows for the final, intermediate and primary (mobile) commodities. Different lengths of run could be considered depending on the definition, or classification of mobile and immobile commodities.

These results could then be compared with "actual" results and the area and magnitude of the departures could be specified. The problem is then narrowed down to ascertaining why the departures exist and what alternatives may be available for adjusting the existing situation.

Theoretically, of course, one could work with all of the industries in the agricultural sector. However, technical data requirements would probably make this approach unmanageable. With this restriction the researcher, in order to reduce the investigation to manageable proportions, would be directed to partial analyses involving one industry or a group of highly related industries. Such partial analyses would be useful standing alone and additionally when fitted together in speeding the accumulation of knowledge. For example, a simple spatial price-equilibrium analysis for one industry or final commodity would generate estimates of optimum regional prices, flows, output and consumption.

As a basis for action the competitive efficiency model provides a standard of comparison whereby the organization, pricing and distribution for an industry can be gauged relative to this base. The impact or value of this approach rests on two considerations. First, a set of "standard conditions" is defined which facilitates rigor in thinking and communication. Second, the competitive "standard conditions" model will usually be highly correlated with, and/or part of economic and general welfare models. When "what is" and "what could be" differ, possible areas for choice or action are indicated. Whether or not action will be taken of course will depend on the social goals to be pursued. In this context about all the economist can do is to make clear the economic consequences of alternative courses of action.

Description and Prediction

1. For some purposes it may be desired to describe the evolution of an industry or industries over time. When description

is desired, finite Markov chains and the Leonteif input-
output techniques offer two possible approaches. The
finite Markov chain technique could be employed to indicate how certain of the structural attributes of an industry
have changed over time. The Leonteif input-output approach could be used to show quantitatively how industries
are related in production and, therefore, provides a summary view of the industry structure of the agricultural
sector.

2. Prediction as it relates to market structure could be approached in at least two general ways:

a. Given the descriptive data for an industry and the accompanying transition matrices for certain structural
attributes, Markov chain analyses could be completed
to suggest the future path that the structural attributes
will follow over time. As an indication of "long-run
tendencies," the equilibrium vectors could be derived
for the alternative regular transition matrices.

Given the interdependence coefficients from input-
output analysis, one could predict how industry output
levels would be disturbed with alternative final desired bills of goods. These input models could be combined with programming models to provide capacity,
output and locational treatment of industries in the agricultural sectors under alternative predicted or specified market conditions. In addition, the consistency of
predictions from each of the above approaches could be
checked.

Alternatively, activity analysis models could be employed which would ignore the existing structure of industries in the agricultural sector. In this type of analysis the capacity and location of firms as they currently
exist would be ignored and the "ideal" industry structures would be generated, given regional demands, mobile and immobile resources, firm cost relations and
transport costs. This information, generated independently of existing plant capacity, location and institutional
restrictions, etc. (the long-run special case), might
give some clues to the future adjustments of industries
in the agricultural sector.

b. An alternative way to approach prediction as it relates
to market structure research is consideration of the
variables whose path over time it would be useful to

predict. Thus, information is provided for future industry adjustments; i.e., in addition to restricting firm activity in an industry via antitrust action, for example,
consider useful information to help them make the
"right" adjustments. In this context, information such
as the future levels and location of final commodity
demands, location and level of available resources or
intermediate product supplies, long-run plant cost
relations, etc., might be of great value in providing
better data for firm decision-making purposes.

Chapter 9

REPORT OF WORKGROUP 3A
Paul E. Nelson, Jr., Chairman
U.S. Department of Agriculture

| *Operational criteria for evaluating market performance of firms and industries in food marketing and processing*

OPERATIONAL EVALUATION OF PERFORMANCE

T HE PRIMARY DIFFERENTIATION between dimensions and norms is that dimensions are a mechanism of operational measurement whereas norms offer a basis for judgment. Each of the dimensions is identified and for discussion purposes, data series and data sources available to operationally quantify each dimension are suggested. Each dimension is then considered in terms of a possible norm or a combination of norms suggested by Sosnick's chapter.

The character of the material precluded the development of complete consensus. Some of the divergence of opinion in Workgroup 3A is reflected in Table 9.1, where some of the dimensions suggested by Sosnick were placed in three categories: I. Crucial; II. Very Important; III. Important.

Table 9.1. Market Performance Dimension

Rankings With Respect to Importance	I	II	III
Production efficiency	5		
Technological progressiveness	4	1	
Product suitability	1	4	
Profit rates	4	1	
Level of output	1		4
Exchange efficiency	4	1	
Cost of sales promotion	1	2	2
Unethical practices	1	1	3
External effects		1	4
Labor relations	2	1	2

1. Production Efficiency (includes distribution).

   a. Here the dimension will consist of data which are synthesized from observed data of specified establishments and a given state of technology. These synthesized data may be used to construct an optimum establishment. Current operations will furnish information concerning the present condition of plants in respect to their operations.

   b. The norm is simply the consideration that movement towards the optimum is evidence of adequate performance.

2. Technological Progressiveness

   a. In applying the dimension of production efficiency the dimension of technological progressiveness simultaneously should be applied. The data of technological progressiveness will show up in new capital expenditures and the adoption of new types of equipment identified as such. Capital expenditure data may be obtained for most industries from the Census of Manufacturers and from the Annual Survey of Manufacturers. Identification of quality of the equipment primarily must come from special studies, which will involve conversations with equipment companies selling to these industries.

   b. In the case of technological progressiveness improvement is the norm, as adoption of new items and the budget expenditures for new equipment together would be considered evidence of satisfactory performance.

3. Product Suitability

   a. Individual products or services are susceptible to empirical testings and consumer panel evaluations. Groups such as the Bureau of Standards, the Consumers Union, Consumers Research and various trade publications report the prices and information needed to evaluate the capability of commodities and services. In addition, consumer panel tests can serve as a source of data with respect to consumer attitudes toward items purchased and used.

   b. The norm for product suitability is difficult if not impossible to establish. Brands should reflect real differences. Product and package variety should be available at appropriate cost differentials to the consumer, e.g.,

different package sizes. Package sizes other than the
modal unit should reflect the higher costs for producing
such packaged units. Illustratively, in some communities milk in half-gallon containers would be the modal
package size, and gallon, quart and pint containers would
reflect the additional costs for running products in these
sizes. In other communities the gallon jugs might be
the modal container; in this instance quarts and half
gallons would reflect the differential cost.

4. Profit Rates

a. Figures such as percent of return on net worth or assets
would be collected; percent of profit return of sales also
would be used. Internal Revenue Source Book and various industry periodicals such as Moody's, Dunn and
Bradstreet and Fortune provide information for many
industries and companies. Before the ratios are computed, efforts should be made (if data enabled such
manipulations) to be sure that the total profit included
such things as unusual executive bonuses.

b. The norm for profit rates could be the going rate of
bank interest. This would be a per se norm with which
many will disagree. The feeling is that not only rates
but also stability of the rate over time, entry and exit
should be considered.

5. Output Restriction

a. Data will be available only through the industry con-
tact and this type will be difficult if not impossible
to obtain.

b. The group could not agree upon an operational norm.

6. Exchange Efficiency

a. Exchange efficiency is a dimension which encompasses
data obtained by trade studies concerning grading, inspection, market information, studies relating to cross
hauls, studies relating price flexibilities (some prices
could be too flexible to be efficient). The group considered that although duplicate delivery routes are similar to cross hauls, they have different aspects sufficient
to make them important enough to be treated separately.

b. The norm in this instance is the perfect market.

7. Cost of Sales Promotion

   a. Source Book of Internal Revenue Service, Printer's Ink, Food Field Reporter, Advertising Age.

   b. Advertising is justified when it decreases production costs through higher volume and when the cost reduction is passed on to the consumer. Also tied to this is the fact that information given the consumer should be accurate and directed toward helping him make a reasoned selection among product alternatives. How this norm is to be measured is a continuing problem. Individual and company studies concerning production costs and pricing would be the only way to operationally quantify this norm.

8. Unethical Practices

   a. Results of unethical practices will show up under exchange efficiency, technological progressiveness and productive efficiency. Certain unethical practices, such as fraud and false advertising, are in themselves dimensions.

   b. Section 5 of the Federal Trade Commission Act can serve as a basis for defining standards of advertising. Close conformance of ads with this legal norm would indicate satisfactory performance.

9. Participant Rationality

   a. This dimension really is included in exchange efficiency, and relates particularly to the type of information provided by testing groups such as the Bureau of Standards and Consumers Union. Participant rationality is the use of such information in an exchange situation.

10. Conservation

   a. The conservation concept is not as clearly applicable in food processing and food marketing as in food and fiber production. Any effect would be upon allocation of resources on the farm as they respond to the pricing of foods in the processing and marketing channels. Misallocations due to imperfection of pricing dimensions could affect conservation problems at the production level.

11. External Effects

   a. The dimension consists of identifiable items such as
      water pollution and unpleasant odors from processing
      establishments, such as slaughtering houses. It seems
      that this dimension can be quantified through such spe-
      cific items which would be discovered by field research.

   b. The norm is obvious; none of these should be permitted.

12. Labor Relations

   a. Dimensions would include case studies or surveys of
      establishments concerning their hiring policies, their
      training programs, work conditions and work practices.
      Such policies would include the hiring of underprivi-
      leged and handicapped persons in positions where they
      could have an opportunity to contribute productively.

   b. The norms would exclude such devices as feather-
      bedding, sweatshops, work stoppages. The norms
      would include sharing of productivity increases. On-
      the-spot observations are a possible way to quantify
      such norms.

SUMMARY

   These dimensions frequently must be clustered, some may
overlap and in some instances they may actually be contradictory.
Certain norms frequently clash. For example, efficiency and variety of product are inherently contradictory. Attempts to use
these norms and quantify them should stimulate new ideas and new
ways of quantification. Until economists can develop quantitative
means for identifying dimensions and establishing norms, they
will not be able to assist society to the extent their profession is
obligated.

Chapter 10

REPORT OF WORKGROUP 3B
Harold Breimyer, Chairman
U.S. Department of Agriculture

Criteria for evaluating
performance norms
of firms and industries

I N ADDRESSING OURSELVES to the structure-conduct-performance approach to industrial organization we join in the process of development of economic doctrine. We stand on the frontier of that development, not in the central city. We see this doctrinal evolution as arising from the inadequacy of the body of theory that, while originating as recently as the mid-1920's, has now become "conventional." In particular, many of the structural concepts employed in models of imperfect competition are indeterminate with respect to predicting performance. We most assuredly do not reject conventional structural theory insofar as it is useful. We only recognize that it is not entirely sufficient.

NEW THEORY FOR INDUSTRIAL ORGANIZATION

It is not certain that the structural-conduct-performance triad is entirely satisfactory. The 12 criteria proposed by Sosnick are not of logically equivalent categories, are somewhat inconsistent and are not mutually exclusive. One member of our workgroup even dubbed them a "hodgepodge." Yet we were entirely respectful toward them as adequate in the present stage of evolution of a new theory system for industrial organization.

The performance approach is essentially normative. It is an expression of welfare concepts. Moreover, being unsystematic it can be labelled as "common sense" in nature. This system will be more useful when the values and ideals implicit in the criteria can be identified with some precision.

Not incidentally, we added, without concern for numerology, a 13th criterion: adaptability to change.

The economic system — as well as legal and other systems — a society develops invariably incorporates to some degree the

values and mores that society holds dear. Since an evaluation of
performance norms is implicitly normative, it is helpful to re-
mind ourselves of some of the values of our own contemporary
society.

Performance

In entertaining the question, "Why emphasize performance?",
the group first considered the relation of performance norms to
societal norms, e.g., growth, stability and employment and the
crucial importance of production efficiency. These in turn
aroused excursions into the realm of individual values in a democratic society. The values cited included equity, freedom, respect for the individual, security, access to opportunity, consumer
choice, level and distribution of income, dispersion of economic
power, remuneration commensurate with services rendered and
a pragmatic attitude. Group values were cited also as distinct
from aggregate or societal goals and business goals. The latter
were never clearly delineated, however, from the few group values
that were cited. Finally, some doubts occurred as to the desirability of a long list of performance norms, though it was observed
that a long list could be shortened once specific markets were
identified and evaluated.

The beauty of the perfectly competitive model, which economists relied on so long, is that it conformed to these values with
a minimum of inconsistency or conflict. For example, attractive
to us are its connotations of smallness; the ease of entry built
into the models and especially the absolute uniformity of prices
for both factors and products that result under it. Habitually our
profession has disregarded its weaknesses, such as that it would
tend to produce standardized products, in denial of the heterogeneity
of preferences held by consumers. Also, economists have often
shown rather little concern for the many obstacles to perfect
competition that exist in the real world. Overlooked has been the
fact that a competitive model must work all the way — that is to
say, perfectly, with full employment of resources — to work at
all well. Otherwise, the marginality principle exploits the disadvantaged. But these limitations are not serious if a close approximation to a perfectly competitive model exists. Furthermore, one big attraction of the perfectly competitive model is
that it lends itself to reduction to mathematical equations, a consideration in which, among economists, familiarity breeds not
contempt but deep affection.

Once there is a clear and substantial departure from the

competitive model, the situation becomes scrambled. We then
face serious conflicts of values. Sosnick's 12-point listing of
performance norms is a way of disciplining us to take account of
the many aspects of performance when evaluating how well a
given industry meets the welfare goals of society.

Our group would have preferred a more systematic and orderly set of concepts. Some members were impatient with the
subjective, or nonmeasurable, or judgmental, approaches called
for. They even proposed that a satisfactory outcome is not possible until a tighter system is devised. However, the majority
acquiesced in recognizing and accepting the present partial state
of our knowledge.

When a critical judgment of market structure reveals deficiencies, there follows an implication that a remedy may be
available. We failed to resolve the subsequent question as to
whether remedial action becomes, in turn, a part of (redefined)
structure. Lending support to an affirmative answer is an urgent
desire for predictive structural models.

CRITERIA EXAMINED

The 13 performance criteria do not fall naturally into any
rank order. We distinguished between static and dynamic aspects. How acceptable an industry may be in temporal cross-
section does not necessarily tell us what may be expected over
time. For prediction we implicitly resort to structural analysis.
That is, how can we predict the future except by deciding what
present structure promises to bring forth? In order to attain
predictability we need also to be able to draw on empirical
studies. It is to be hoped that a number will be forthcoming.

We had another reason for hesitating to rank the 13 criteria.
It is that not only may they vary in their conformity to welfare
goals of society, but they differ in (1) their susceptibility to observation and (2) their adaptability to private or public remedial
action. Further, the relative importance of the several criteria
must surely vary among industries.

We gave most attention to the interrelated criteria of technological efficiency and progressiveness, output volume and
price-marginal cost ratio. These are to considerable extent
various aspects of a single economic function. In addition, some
of our group placed great stress on the criterion of exchange efficiency, but they also confessed the extreme difficulty in grap-
pling with it analytically.

The usefulness of profit ratio as a criterion received as

much discussion as it may have deserved, but not as much as was necessary for its resolution. Nevertheless, there was some agreement that irrespective of whether profit is a valuable criterion per se, the persistence of an unusually high or unusually low rate of profit over time should be a signal to further inquiry along the lines of other criteria.

Oligopoly and Monopoly

An interesting and not unexpected focus of conversation was how to judge a well-behaved oligopoly or monopoly. If an industry has structural capability for anti-welfare performance but at the time of observation is benign if not beneficent, what conclusion is to be reached? We did not resolve this, but our lingering desire for a predictive structural model suggested that we distrusted apparent good behavior that is not grounded in a structural imperative.

Members of our group were interrogated as to how useful they believe performance criteria to be as an aid in designing research into the structure of the market for farm products. The response was unanimously favorable. Several reasons for the accolade were revealed. One is that the criteria serve as noto bene reminders of what we should look for. Another reason advanced is that the outline of 12 or more performance criteria affords precaution against concentrating on one or a few criteria to the exclusion of others. One or two members of the group who had utilized performance criteria in their research testified to its applicability and worthwhileness.

Chapter 11

REPORT OF WORKGROUP 4

Paul L. Farris, Chairman

Purdue University

Impact of factors external to the market on the organization and behavior of firms *

NUMEROUS FACTORS external to the market affect market structure, conduct and performance. They are broadly classified as government activities, technological developments, factor markets, physical properties of products and general economic conditions. External influences go beyond market structure interrelations, such as effects of structure on conduct, of conduct on performance or of conduct and performance on structure. They also refer to influences aside from motivating forces of management, which originate within the firm. External factors are especially significant determinants of market structure change in the long run.

Government activities constitute one of the largest set of external influences on market structure and conduct. Antitrust actions affect industry concentration. Trade practice regulations directly influence conduct. Government price support programs alter market organization and behavior through demand and supply expansion or contraction. Government-erected trade barriers, tariffs and quotas can change the number of firms in a market or the domestic market share. Facilitating government legislation, such as the Capper Volstead Act and patent laws, affect firm growth, market organization and market behavior.

Technology is a second important external area in market structure study. Some technological developments that affect industry structure originate outside the industry. Improved interstate highways combined with new packaging and handling techniques have shrunk distances and combined isolated markets. Some external technological developments interact with and modify developments and innovations within particular industries. Technological considerations underlie scale economies, which in turn cause or permit market structures to change in particular

*The assistance and suggestions of Hugh L. Moore, Purdue University, and Allen B. Paul, USDA, are hereby acknowledged in the preparation of this report.

directions. In some instances there may be significant interrelations between market structure and technological change, with
directions of causation running both ways.

The availability of particular production factors varies among
industries and kinds of firms. Capital sources available to large
firms may not be available to small ones; or the terms on which
capital is made available may differ among firms and industries.
Highly skilled management and labor may be in scarce supply and
differentially available to various firms and industries.

The physical properties of products produced or handled may
also alter market structure. Highly perishable and bulky items
of low value have limited market areas, whereas items that are
more durable and of high value relative to weight would be expected to have larger marketing areas. Changes in physical properties of products affect market dimensions and in turn market
structure.

Product demand and supply conditions help mold market structures. Variations in demand brought about by changing economic
conditions and consumer preferences can greatly alter market
organization. Changes might be gradual or sudden, consistently
in the same direction or alternately increasing and decreasing.
The nature of a change may give rise to a particular direction of
change in market structure.

POSSIBLE RESEARCH AREAS

The following list of examples is not all-inclusive but is intended to be illustrative of some possible specific directions for
research.

Reorientation of Antitrust Policy

Antitrust policy is now mostly concerned with preventing
greater industry concentration through mergers and with attacking per se restraints of trade such as price-fixing, division of
markets and exclusionary practices. Future policy might seek
structural reorganization to achieve greater competitive performance, more progressive technological innovation and greater freedom of entry into areas where market decisions, price policy and
competitive behavior are determined. New legislation may be
necessary to achieve these goals.

Research, on an industry basis, might be devoted to such
areas as the feasibility of restructuring key industries based on

differentials between technical efficiency and firm capacity, de-concentrating highly concentrated industries, reducing barriers to entry where fewness leads to restrained competition and modifying certain characteristics of large established firms, such as degree of integration, product diversification, distribution organization and other structural factors.

Effects of Shifts in Demand

A gradually expanding demand might be expected to result in an easing of adjustments to technological and economic impacts — small firms remaining in business longer and large firms expanding to take advantage of the increased demand. A rapid expansion of demand might allow aggressive new entries into the market, affecting the number and size of firms, market behavior and technological innovation. Decreasing demand might result in increased pressure to eliminate weak competitors, expand advertising and sales promotion activities, integrate various functions and abandon obsolete plants. Demand shifts which alternate from one year to the next may give rise to particular types of market organization.

Research could be oriented toward determining relations between various kinds of demand shifts and changes in market structure and behavior. Results might suggest kinds of government or group policies to facilitate adjustment of certain firms to demand changes or to encourage certain directions of change in market structure. Research might also attempt to determine the probable impact of potential demand changes or demand stabilization programs upon market structure and behavior.

Impacts of Financial Conditions

An example of an important financial issue concerns the effect of a change in monetary policy on the ability of different firms to command resources in competition with each other. While the intent of a tight money policy in curbing inflation may be to stay neutral with respect to market structure, there is a legitimate doubt that the effect is neutral. One presumption is that large firms have a relative advantage over small firms; another is that fast-growing firms are more sensitive to changes in monetary policy than small firms. Still other hypotheses may prevail.

To ascertain the effects of a change in monetary policy, a basic description of how funds flow into the food marketing system

would be required. It would be necessary to know not only the
roles of banks, insurance companies and the like, but also the
roles of various merchants, brokers and input suppliers in providing funds. Were such descriptions available, one could take a
particular action, like tight money or subsidized loans, and trace
it through the system. An appraisal could be made of various effects of the action, including compensating actions within the
financial system.

Changes in Regulation, Facilities and
Technology in Transportation

It is generally believed that agricultural markets tend to be
enlarged by decreases in transportation costs. Research might
be directed toward ascertaining specific effects of rate changes,
transportation technology and facilities on market structure and
behavior in particular industries. Some of the changes which
might be studied include: the Transportation Act of 1958 which
permitted freight rate cuts to be made by one type of carrier without regard to their effects on another type of carrier; changes in
the exemption from regulation of unprocessed agricultural commodities hauled by trucks; reductions in the number of barges
that may be pushed by one boat; the interstate highway system;
the St. Lawrence Seaway; city bypasses and expressways; and
specific examples of technology such as larger, lighter, faster
and better refrigerated trucks; truck-train piggyback transportation systems; and the development of lightweight nonreturnable
packages, such as paper packages for milk.

Cooperative Organization

Cooperatives owe their peculiar legal and tax structure to
government legislation. Differences in the legal structure of cooperatives suggest the need to investigate the consideration which
noncooperative firms take of cooperative dividends in their pricing
policy. Other research questions might be concerned with differences in acceptable profits between cooperatives and noncoopera-
tives and effects of differences on total profits in the industry.
Attention could also be directed toward determining effects the
cooperative form of organization may have on other patterns of
behavior and on directions of change in market structure over
time.

Special Government Programs

There is a wide variety of government programs in agriculture. Examples include market orders, food distribution programs and price support programs. The programs cannot be presumed to be neutral in respect to market structure and behavior. Some market orders set minimum prices; some control the quality of shipments; still others impose quotas on shipments. Some government price support programs remove from the open market a substantial quantity of a commodity, either by purchases or by loans to producers. The quantity removed must be stored, resulting in changes in storage capacity and storage firms. Changes in volumes handled in traditional marketing channels may influence behavior patterns and structural changes of firms in these channels and elsewhere. Important research questions concern the effects of various special government programs on market structure and behavior in particular industries and markets where the programs operate.

Service and Educational Activities of Governmental Agencies

It is generally believed that improved knowledge about the product, about current market conditions and about the future encourages more competitive markets. Government service and educational programs provide knowledge of the kind required to increase the effective functioning of exchange processes. Over time improved market knowledge can change the structure of an industry by encouraging growth and survival of those firms with real cost advantages.

Research efforts can be oriented in two main directions. One would be to ascertain precise information needs of buyers and sellers in particular markets from farm to retail in order to improve skills in the exchange process. The results could lead to making government service and education programs more specific and accurate in terms of objectives they are designed to accomplish. The second research orientation would attempt to determine the consequences of particular service and education programs on market performance and, over time, on directions of change in market structure. There could be opportunity in some cases to combine both orientations in the same research undertaking. Results should contribute to our ability to appraise the role and effectiveness of service and educational programs as one policy alternative in dealing with various market structure problems.

PART FIVE

SUMMARY

Chapter 12

WINN F. FINNER
U.S. Department of Agriculture
and
R. G. BRESSLER, JR.
University of California

SUMMARY REMARKS

D R. WINN FINNER, Economic Research Service, USDA: I am pleased to see several evidences of new research efforts and interests in market structure — a field which has come under some criticism during the past several years.

This criticism arose partly in the following way. In the 1930's there was a sizable development, both empirically and theoretically, concerning market structure research. This of course had been preceded by original thinking going back into the nineteenth century, if not earlier. It was during the 1930's that the Temporary National Economic Committee conducted extensive hearings and fostered a program of research dealing with changes in market organization and competition and the way these changes were influencing the economic performance of different industries. Likewise during this period, the work of Chamberlin, Robinson and others came to be widely known by economists; and a number of studies were developed to employ these concepts in explaining the functioning of industries and in evaluating price and production policies of these industries. Then, with due respect to Mason, Bain, Sosnick and a few others, we saw a generation pass during which we largely marked time.

It might be contended that we marked time because the work in the '30's indicated that further research would be fruitless. I do not accept this conclusion even though admitting the logical possibility of it. Even if we admit this possibility, however, I believe that much remained unreconciled. Do we, for example, agree with W. H. Nicholls regarding market imperfections in the cigarette industry and that the fragmentation of cigarette companies into a larger number of smaller companies would improve the industry? Or do we agree with A. C. Hoffmann that substantial benefits have accrued to society from concentration of economic activities into fewer firms, and that the imperfections that may arise because of such concentration can be controlled and in any case are small relative to the economies made possible by growing scale?

166

For the many who believe that market structure research is a fruitful area and has an important role to play, there was the fear that the empirical developments of 25 years ago would be largely sacrificed because of such matters as undue attention to the development of a theoretical framework for analysis without sufficient regard for the pragmatic conditions existing in agricultural industries. Closely related to the above point was the concern that we would become mired in definitional and conceptual problems and thus further delay appraisals of market performance. This point of view does not minimize the importance of a logical and adequate conception of a firm, a product, an industry or a market, but it does insist that operationally usable concepts should be formulable which can enable research concerning the central issues in market structure to proceed. That is to say, part of our research efforts should certainly be devoted to an improvement of our understanding of basic concepts, tools and methods; but some of our resources should be used wholly to make the best assessments we can at present of the performance of different segments of the marketing system, using those means which are now available and have empirical application.

The work of NCR-20, and no doubt other groups and individuals of the past few years, is providing a solid base for laying to rest the misgivings or criticisms to which I refer above. Within the field of empirical investigation, of course, there are a multitude of problems. I shall consider briefly two of them.

PROFIT RATIOS

The first is the problem of what interpretation to give to specific observed phenomena. Consider profit ratios, for example. Suppose that we know that a given industry is earning 20 percent on its invested capital over a period of time and that we have adequately dealt with such related points as the measurement of the value of this capital. If this industry were a large manufacturer of automobiles, no doubt there are those who would suspect that there were sharp marketing imperfections requiring at least widespread publicity, if not FTC or similar controls regarding conditions of entry, differentiated products and the like. If, however, the industry earning 20 percent on invested capital were Southern agriculture, I suspect that the line of reasoning of many would be quite different. We would be mainly concerned with ways of increasing capital inputs in this sector and the ways to facilitate this adjustment. In other words, there would be quite divergent judgment with respect to the levels of performance in these two industries, or at least the conditions which would improve future performance. Similar differences with respect to other measures of performance, I think, are likely to appear.

PERFORMANCE

The second problem concerns the specific aspects of performance that should be emphasized in research. Sosnick dealt extensively with this in his chapter and I will simply refer to the first point on his list, namely, "What are the potential economies from a better organization of resources employed in marketing firms?" This aspect of performance, in my opinion, deserves greater attention, not so much for the purpose of determining small changes possible at many places in the marketing system, but rather from the standpoint of assessing the possibilities of major efficiencies in selected industries.

Work at Nebraska, for example, suggests the technical possibility of reducing resources used in bread baking and distribution sufficiently so that retail price reductions of more than one-third might be accomplished. Research at Iowa State seems to suggest the possibility that margins obtaining in food retailing might possibly be reduced by approximately the same magnitude if substantial reorganization were undertaken for the purpose of reducing costs. These two may well be beyond any realistic hope of achievement, and possibly the achievement of them might so affect marketing services or other conditions as to make them undesirable ends. Nevertheless, it seems to me that further research concerning problems of this magnitude would be most useful in providing a better framework for assessing the effects that particular changes may have as well as longer run possibilities.

Perhaps we could remove the stigma from economists which Fritz Mueller implies in the last sentence of his statement: "Although economists have contributed much toward the development and enforcement of our antitrust laws, it is fortunate indeed that the development and enforcement of these laws did not await empirical verification of the relevant relationships between market structure and market performance." This is a charge which I think should concern us and which I think we should work to correct, whether it pertains to regulatory activities or to other forces influencing marketing firms. Greater effort directed to performance criteria, I am sure, will be a major avenue for bringing this about.

Professor R. G. BRESSLER, JR., University of California: First, I am impressed by the fact that we are quite concerned with the effects of market structure on the performance of more or less typical firms, but have not concerned ourselves with the ways in which certain special types of firms may react. It is possible that, in situations which might seem undesirable in terms of performance, we may be able to find (or to construct) certain types of firms which would avoid or at least minimize the apparent difficulties. Let me illustrate.

It is a common observation that in local aspects of marketing we find ourselves in a dilemma — we can have either a relatively large number of small, high-cost plants (or stores), or we can restrict the number to one or two large and efficient units — but this exposes us to the difficulty of some kind of monopolistic exploitation. If we can devise a type of firm whose interests and goals are consistent with the interests and goals of the exploited group, however, this dilemma can be avoided. In this example, a cooperative seems the obvious answer — and this was in fact a major consideration in the early development of agricultural cooperatives. Possibly we should devote more time to this type of organization, where the goals of firms or industry are more closely identified with those of society.

A second item is inspired directly by Winn Finner's remarks on rationalized systems of bread baking and distribution which might reduce the price to consumers to 10 cents per loaf. Such research has a very real connection with structure and performance — but very little with structure and performance as discussed in this volume. Such developments require massive revolutions in structure, while most market economists deal only with small changes. Perhaps a better statement is that such programs involve massive and deliberate changes in structure, while most students of market organization stress adjusting to given structures and are not greatly concerned with the possibilities of modifying the market institutions. Some of us, I believe, are prone to accept market institutions as given and not subject to change — and so to rule out some truly spectacular gains that may be possible in marketing.

EFFICIENCY MODELS

This leads me to remark briefly on the use of "efficiency" models in market organization research. I will not attempt to develop the concepts of efficiency models, but I will say that — as our programmers have discovered — these are closely related to the concepts of perfect competition. These efficiency models have a considerable content that is consistent with and important to the concepts of general or social welfare. While I believe that this is very important, please note that this does not mean that I believe: (1) that it is possible or desirable to "return to the system of competitive economics" or (2) that the efficiency model defines the desirable social choice. But I do believe most emphatically that such studies can point out areas where there is a considerable amount of public interest — therefore, areas in which intensive research is justified.

The general approach to studies in market organization involves descriptions of such attributes as numbers of firms, concentration ratios and product differentiation. These descriptions are then the basis for general classifications — competition, monopoly, monopolistic competition and so on. Classifications in turn, coupled with theoretical reasoning, give rise to statements as to performance — more properly, to hypotheses as to possible performance. In this process the description and classification phases may be thought of as a screening process whereby potentially important areas for more detailed investigations are identified.

I believe that this is valid, or at least that the process can be used to eliminate some areas where market imperfections are probably minor. Beyond that, I would urge the use of some efficiency models — and remember that these may be simple or complex — to give a further screening of potential trouble spots. Comparisons of model results with actual results in terms of costs, prices, and output not only suggest these trouble spots, but give at least a rough estimate of the magnitudes of distortions created by the market institutions. Note that this is a diagnostic tool to locate trouble spots — and not necessarily a prescription as to what can or should be done. Following this screening, intensive and detailed studies of the institutions should be made to determine how changes in institutions will affect performance. Finally, the research results are presented to society — in "before-and-after" terms — so that decisions can be made as to what actions if any are wanted.

Let me conclude by emphasizing these last points. I do not believe that institutions are sacred; society can and often does take action to change them. I do not believe that research tells society what it should do, or that the researcher becomes society's decision maker. Rather, research provides meaningful information on the basis of which social choices are made. We can differentiate between technical feasibility and practicality: the first indicates what can be done, the second what society wants to do. I do not believe that researchers should shun particular research areas because they have preconceived notions as to

society's interest or lack of interest in change; no more do I believe that researchers should try to make decisions for society.
The role of the researcher is to do research and to make known
his results. Society, confronted with the right kind of research
results, is then in a position to make intelligent decisions. In
this manner, research makes its contribution in influencing actions and modifying institutions.

K

Kennedy, Thomas, 48
Kerr, Clark, 45, 48
Knight, F. H., 42
Kohls, R. L., 8-18
Kreps, T. J., 81
Kuhn, Alfred, 47

L

Labor organizations, 44-53
  effect of on market structure,
    46-50
Labor relations, 124-25, 156
Leibenstein, Harvey, 11, 12, 16
Levinson, H. M., 44, 45
Liabilities, composition of, 39
Lindblom, C. E., 46
Loan intermediary, firm as, 36-40
Loans, cost and availability of, 23-
  27
Losses, unjustified, 107-8

M

Machlup, Fritz, 49
Malmgren, H. B., 15
Management, role of, 140-43
  and administrative processes,
    143
  and behavior of firms, 143
  development of strategies, 142-
    43
  in gathering and analysing infor-
    mation, 141-42
  goal formulation, 142
  and managerial resources, 142
Managerial goals and values, 138-
  44
Market
  agricultural, 1-7
  behavior of and goals and values,
    138-44
  boundaries of, 29-31
  commodity, 19-36
  conduct of, defined, 1
  organization of, defined, 1
Market performance
  and alternatives, 104-7

clarifications of, 82-85
concept of, 81-85
and conservation, 121-23
and cost of sales promotion, 116-
  19
criteria for evaluating, 81-137
defined, 1
dimension norms for, 92-125
dimensions of, 85-92, 152
evaluating, 152-56
and exchange efficiency, 112-16
and external effects, 123-24
and labor relations, 124-25
and level of output, 108-10
and overproduction, 110-12
and participant rationality, 120-21
and product suitability, 97-99
and production efficiency, 92-95
and profit, 100-104
and progressiveness, 95-97
and social welfare, 73-77
and unethical practices, 119
Market structure, 19-43
  as analytical idea, 40-43
  defined, 1
  and labor organizations, 46-50
  and managerial goals and values,
    138-44
Marketing and processing, food, 152-
  56
Markham, J. W., 121
Markowitz, H., 30
Mason, E. S., 126
Means, Gardiner, 135-36
Measurement, 145-51
Merger litigation, 71-72
Mergers, 22-23
Miller, C. J., 36
Mishan, E. J., 124
Mitchell, G. W., 23
Models, efficiency, 169-71
Monopoly, 160
Mueller, W. F., 8, 20, 58, 63, 82,
  134-37, 168

N

Nelson, Paul E., 152-56
Net worth of businesses and sales,
  24